Exploring
EARTH AND SPACE SCIENCE

2

CAL–CON

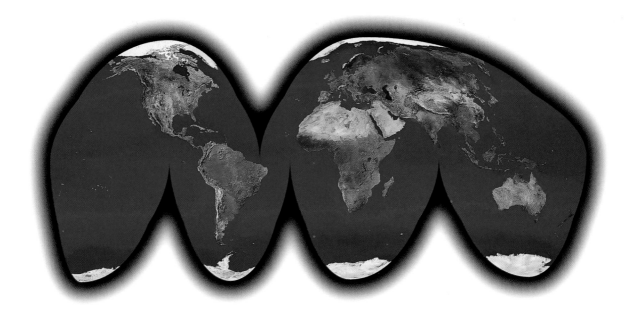

Marshall Cavendish
New York • London • Toronto • Sydney

Marshall Cavendish Corporation
99 White Plains Road
Tarrytown, New York 10591

Website: www.marshallcavendish.com

© 2002 Marshall Cavendish Corporation

Created by **Brown Partworks Limited**

Library of Congress Cataloging-in-Publication Data

Exploring earth and space science.
    p. cm.
   Includes bibliographical references and indexes.
   Contents: 1. Acid and base-Calcium -- 2. Calendar-Continental shelf -- 3. Copper-El
Niño and La Niña -- 4. Energy-Gondwana -- 5. Grassland-Laser -- 6. Light-Meteor -- 7.
Meteorology-Ordovician period -- 8. Ore-Prospecting -- 9. Protein-Star -- 10.
Stratosphere-X ray -- 11. Index.
   ISBN 0-7614-7219-3 (set) -- ISBN 0-7614-7220-7 (v. 1) -- ISBN 0-7614-7221-5 (v. 2)
-- ISBN 0-7614-7222-3 (v. 3) -- ISBN 0-7614-7223-1 (v. 4) -- ISBN 0-7614-7224-X (v.
5) -- ISBN 0-7614-7225-8 (v. 6) -- ISBN 0-7614-7226-6 (v. 7) -- ISBN 0-7614-7227-4
(v. 8) -- ISBN 0-7614-7228-2 (v. 9) -- ISBN 0-7614-7229-0 (v. 10) -- ISBN
0-7614-7230-4 (v. 11)
   1. Earth sciences--Encyclopedias. 2. Space sciences--Encyclopedias. 3.
Astronomy--Encyclopedias

QE5 .E96 2002

550'.3--dc21   00-065801
                                                                              CIP
                                                                              AC

ISBN 0-7614-7219-3 (set)

ISBN 0-7614-7221-5 (vol. 2)

Printed in Hong Kong

06 05 04 03 02 01 00   5 4 3 2 1

Exploring
EARTH AND SPACE SCIENCE

2

CAL–CON

Marshall Cavendish
New York • London • Toronto • Sydney

Calendar

System for dividing and keeping track of time over a period of days, months, or years

Calendars allow people to keep track of the passing days. They help to place events in their chronological order (the order in which they happen). Calendars also help to schedule future events, so people know when to celebrate holidays or when to plant crops. In busy modern times, calendars are relied on for planning.

Throughout history, people have used many different types of calendars. The calendar most commonly used today is called the Gregorian calendar, which was introduced in 1582. The Gregorian calendar is now used in many countries. Other calendars used alongside the Gregorian include the Chinese, Jewish, and Muslim calendars.

Sun and Moon

In ancient times, even before there were calendars, people had observed the cycles of the Sun and Moon. The most obvious cycle is the daily cycle of the day and night. This is called the solar day (*solar* means relating to the Sun). Ancient people also noticed that the Moon

changed (waxed and waned) every 29½ days, a period of time called the lunar month (*lunar* means relating to the Moon). A third natural cycle is the annual 365-day cycle of the seasons, which is called the solar year.

Most calendars, based on these natural cycles, are either solar or lunar calendars. Lunisolar calendars take into account the cycles of both the Sun and the Moon.

The earliest calendars were lunar calendars. They focus mainly on the lunar month of 29½ days. Since it would be awkward to have a half-day in the calendar, most lunar calendars alternate between months of 29 and 30 days. Twelve of these lunar months produce a year of 354 days, which is 11 days short of the solar

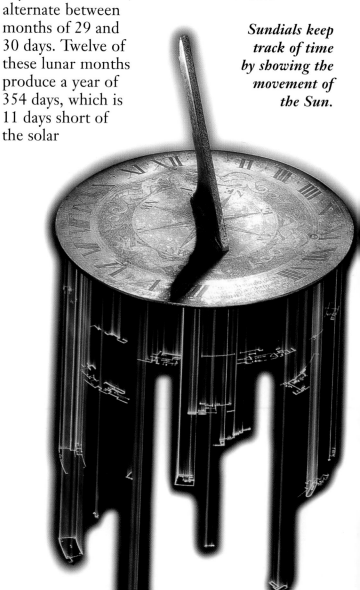

Sundials keep track of time by showing the movement of the Sun.

HIGHLIGHTS

◆ A calendar is a system that marks the passage of time. It is useful for keeping track of past, present, and future events.

◆ The official calendar used in many countries today is the Gregorian calendar. However, other calendars, including the Chinese, Jewish, and Muslim calendars, are also used.

◆ Most calendars are based on natural cycles of the Sun and the Moon. They are based on the lunar month, the solar year, or combine both in a single system.

◆ A system of numbering the years is called an era. The Christian era counts the years from the birth of Christ in the year 1 A.D. (1 C.E.)

year. This shortfall means the dates of the lunar year are not fixed in relation to the seasons. Instead, the dates cycle back through the seasons every 32½ years. This makes lunar calendars rather impractical.

Solar calendars focus on the length of the solar year, the 365 days it takes for Earth to complete one orbit around the Sun. Most solar calendars have months of varying lengths that add up to 365 days. However, the solar year is actually 365¼ days long. Solar calendars take in the extra fraction of a day by regularly adding leap years of 366 days.

The solar year does not contain a whole number of lunar months, which has caused problems since ancient times. Lunisolar calendars therefore occasionally add an extra month to keep up with the Sun. Most lunisolar calendars have 12 lunar months each year but add another month every two or three years.

Ancient calendars

Ancient civilizations used the sky as a calendar, keeping track of the regular movements of the Sun and stars. The progress of the seasons can be measured by charting the exact position of the Sun as it rises in the east throughout the year. The positions of the stars in the night sky can be used in the same way, since each constellation (group of stars) can be seen only at certain times of the year.

Many ancient people kept track of time by using stone structures to mark the position of the Sun and stars. These monuments were built to line up with exact positions in the sky, where a certain star or the Sun might be seen at a certain time of year. Stonehenge, a monument near Salisbury in southern England, is believed to be such one ancient observatory with many of these arrangements built into its design.

Over 3,000 years ago, the ancient Babylonians, who lived in what is now Iraq, used a calendar with 12 months of either 29 or 30 days. To keep their calendar in line with the solar year, an extra month was added three times every eight years.

The Babylonians were among the first people to use a week consisting of seven days. Unlike the year, month, and day, the week is an artificial span of time, not based on any natural cycle.

An example of a lunar calendar from the 17th century, which can be used to calculate the appearance (phase) of the Moon on any given date.

However, many ancient people used the week, probably because it provided a useful span of time between market days. Throughout history, different civilizations have used weeks of various lengths. In West Africa, many people used a four-day week, whereas the Incas of ancient Peru in South America had a ten-day week.

The ancient Egyptians were probably the first people to develop a solar calendar. They measured the length of the year by charting the rising and setting of a bright star now called Sirius. The Egyptians noticed that the annual flood of the Nile River, which was vital to the success of their farming because it provided water and food for their crops, happened soon after Sirius first appeared in the skies on the horizon at dawn. They established a 365-day calendar by counting the days between these yearly first appearances of Sirius.

Solstices and Equinoxes

The four seasons of the year, spring, summer, fall, and winter, come about because Earth is tilted on its axis. The tilt means that the amount of sunlight that reaches a given spot on Earth varies throughout the year. At the spring equinox, around March 21, and the autumn equinox, around September 23, there are 12 hours of daylight and 12 hours of night everywhere on the planet. In the Northern Hemisphere, the summer solstice (around June 21) is the longest day of the year. On this day, the Sun rises as far north of due east as it ever does. Winter solstice (around December 22) is the shortest day in the Northern Hemisphere. On this day, the Sun rises as far south of due east as it ever does.

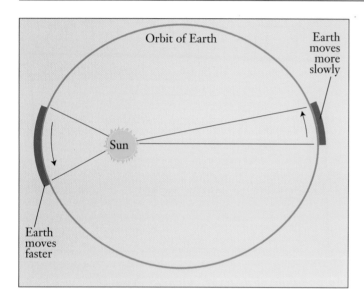

The Sun is not a good timekeeper because Earth has an elliptical (oval) orbit. Earth moves more rapidly along this orbit when it is near the Sun than when it is farther away. Therefore the Sun's speed along its path does not appear to remain the same.

Roman calendars

Roman calendars may date back as far as the 8th century B.C.E. The first Roman calendar had 10 lunar months, giving a year of 304 days. The months were Martius, Aprilis, Maius, Junius, Quintilis, Sextilis, September, October, November, and December. Two extra months, January and February, were added later. These 12 months added up to 355 days, still short of the solar year. An extra month of 22 or 23 days was added every other year to make up the difference. This was an improvement, but the Roman calendar was still not accurate enough.

By the time of Julius Caesar (100–44 B.C.E.) the Roman calendar had advanced a full three months ahead of the seasons. Caesar decided to establish a more accurate calendar, and he asked an astronomer named Sosigenes for help. Sosigenes recommended a calendar, now called the Julian calendar, with a 365-day year, but with every fourth year a leap year of 366 days.

Julius Caesar was murdered in 44 B.C.E. Later, the month of Quintilis was renamed Julius (now July) in his honor. The next emperor, Augustus Caesar, decided to honor himself in the same way. He had the eighth month renamed Augustus (now August).

Gregorian calendar

The Julian calendar was used well into the 16th century. However, it gradually fell behind because it took the length of the solar year to be 365 days and 6 hours. The exact length is 365 days, 5 hours, 48 minutes, and 46 seconds. Eleven minutes may seem a small error, but in the course of 1,600 years, it added up to a shortfall of about 10 days.

In the 1580s, Pope Gregory XIII decided to solve this problem. He consulted the German astronomer Christoph Clavius. Clavius suggested the calendar could be improved by refining the schedule of leap years. Instead of having leap years every four years, as in the Julian calendar, leap years would be added every fourth year except at the start of each new century whose number could not be exactly divided by 400. In practice this meant the years 1600 and 2000 would be leap years, but the years 1700, 1800, or 1900 would not.

This small change made the new calendar, now called the Gregorian calendar, much more accurate. The Gregorian year varies from the

The Gregorian calendar, the world's official calendar, was named for Pope Gregory XIII (right) in the 16th century. It is an extremely accurate calendar, taking over 3,000 years before it is wrong by one day.

true length of the solar year by only 26 seconds. It takes 3,300 years for it to be off by a single day. Today the Gregorian calendar is the official calendar in many countries.

Eras

Once a calendar has been established, the next question is where to begin numbering the years. Different cultures have settled on different starting points.

Any system of numbering the years is called an era. The Jewish era, for example, begins at the year taken to be the time of the world's creation. This is said to be the year 3752 B.C.E. according to the Gregorian calendar. The year 2000 in the Gregorian calendar is the year 5760 in the Jewish era.

The Romans numbered the years beginning with the founding of Rome in 753 B.C.E. The system most people use today for numbering the years, the Christian era, was put forward by a monk called Dionysius Exiguus in 525 C.E. He suggested numbering the years from the birth of Christ, the year A.D 1. *A.D.* stands for *anno Domini,* "the year of our Lord." The year immediately before this year is 1 B.C., meaning "before Christ."

This idea gradually became generally accepted. However, many people now prefer to write B.C.E. (before common era) and C.E. (common era) instead.

Other calendars in use

The Chinese calendar began in 2637 B.C.E., the year that the emperor Huangdi is believed to have invented it. It is a lunisolar calendar that has 12 lunar months of either 29 or 30 days. An extra month is added seven times every 19 years.

In the Chinese calendar, the years are grouped into 60-year cycles. Each 60-year cycle is subdivided into five cycles of 12 years. Each of the 12 years bears the name of one of the following animals: rat, ox, tiger, rabbit, dragon, snake, horse, sheep, monkey, rooster, dog, and pig. The year 2000 in the Gregorian calendar, for example, was the year of the dragon.

The Jewish calendar is a lunisolar calendar that has 12 months of either 29 or 30 days, to follow the cycles of the Moon. Seven times every 19 years, a 13th month is added to keep the calendar in tune with the seasons brought by the Sun.

The Muslim calendar is used throughout the Near and Middle East. It begins on the date when the prophet Mohammed fled from Mecca to Medina: July 16, 622 C.E. according to the Gregorian calendar. The Muslim calendar is a lunar calendar, with a 354-day cycle of 12 lunar months. The Muslim year is about 11 days shorter than the solar year. Therefore the dates move backward through the seasons, taking 32½ years to make a complete cycle.

CHECK THESE OUT!
✔CONSTELLATION ✔DAY
✔EQUINOX AND SOLSTICE
✔MOON ✔SEASON ✔SUN ✔TIME

Cambrian Period

The period of time from about 570 to 505 million years ago

The Cambrian is the earliest time that huge numbers of creatures with shells lived in the oceans of the world. Their fossilized (preserved) remains appear in the lowest and oldest Cambrian strata (STRAH-tuh; rock layers) formed from seabed deposits of the time. This burst of sea life makes the Cambrian one of the most interesting periods in the history of life. The Cambrian is the first period of geological time within the Paleozoic (PAY-lee-uh-ZOH-ik) era, and it began 570 million years ago. The Cambrian lasted for 65 million years.

An explosion of life

Although life in the seas began perhaps around 3.5 billion years ago in Precambrian times, according to recent information, the evolution of life-forms was

HIGHLIGHTS

- The Cambrian period lasted from 570 million to 505 million years ago.

- Fossil shells of sea creatures first appear at the beginning of Cambrian time.

- So many different kinds of organisms are fossilized in early Cambrian rocks that advanced life must have originated in much earlier Precambrian times.

- Most of the continents were joined together to form a supercontinent called Gondwana.

very slow. It was only near the end of Precambrian times that larger creatures with multicelled (many-celled) bodies grew to more than 1 inch (2.5 cm) or so long. However, these Precambrian creatures were thought to have had soft bodies as they have not been fossilized. Some scientists believe they may have become extinct at the end of the Precambrian.

The beginning of the Cambrian is marked by an increase in seabed-burrowing worms and the appearance of tiny fossil shells (¼ inch or 6.25 mm in size). Their fossil remains occur in seabed deposits laid down in the warm, shallow, tropical waters of the time. These earliest fossil shells are preserved after the death of the animals because they are made of hard mineral.

The shells belong to a variety of animals, some of which are distantly related to the snails and squids of today. Many others are extinct forms of arthropods (AHR-thruh-PAHDZ; shrimps and spiders, for example) such as trilobites

*A trilobite fossil called **Paradoxides**. Trilobites were highly developed marine organisms.*

(TRY-luh-BYTS). The development of shells by these creatures may have helped to protect them from predators with teeth and claws.

Cambrian rocks

The World Heritage Site of the Burgess Shale in British Columbia, Canada, has an amazing range of typical Cambrian life preserved in the rock strata there. The Burgess Shale was first discovered in 1909 by U.S. paleontologist (PAY-lee-AHN-TOH-luh-jist; a scientist who studies fossils) Charles Doolittle Walcott (1850–1927) high on the slopes of Mount Field in the Canadian Rocky Mountains.

Walcott dug some 65,000 fossils from these middle Cambrian sedimentary rocks. Most of the fossils were extinct shrimplike arthropods. They included sponges, trilobites, brachiopods (BRAY-kee-uh-PAHDZ), worms, and a tiny eel-shaped animal (2 inches or 5 cm long) that may be the most distant known ancestor of all animals with backbones, including humans. The creatures were probably caught up in a submarine mud slide. It buried them so quickly that some soft

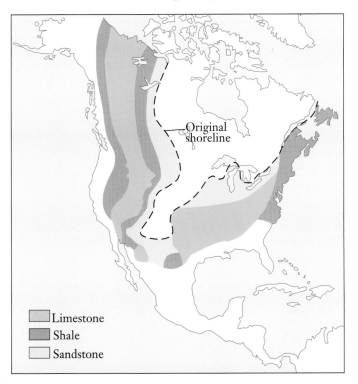

Limestone
Shale
Sandstone

Most of North America was under water during the Cambrian period. Limestone, shale, and sandstone deposits formed around the original shoreline.

LOOK CLOSER

Trilobites

Trilobites are extinct arthropod sea creatures, distantly related to living shrimps, with paired and jointed legs. They look a bit like the living king crabs. Trilobites first appear as fossils in lower Cambrian times and disappear from the rock record at the end of the Permian, some 245 million years ago. Most trilobites lived on the seabed. They ranged in size from barely ⅙ inch (5 mm) to nearly 2½ feet (76 cm). Trilobites had a hard shell made of many hinged pieces, which allowed them to curl up.

body parts such as gills were preserved. These types of fossils do not exist anywhere else, and so the site is protected.

In recent years other spectacular sites with Cambrian fossils have been discovered in China and northernmost Greenland. Scientists think that the variety of organisms preserved in these rocks is so great that their origins must lie in Precambrian times, at least 800 million years ago.

Cambrian Earth

A global map of the Cambrian world shows a quite unrecognizable arrangement of continents and oceans. China, India, Australia, Antarctica, Africa, and South America were joined together as a massive continent called Gondwana (GON-DWAH-nuh), which stretched from pole to pole. North America and Siberia were separate and lay astride the equator, gradually moving northward.

The Cambrian period is named after *Cambria*, the Latin word for Wales. The period was given this name by Adam Sedgwick (1785–1873), a professor of geology (the study of rocks). In the early part of the 19th century, Sedgwick and another geologist, Roderick Murchison, first mapped out rock strata in Wales and showed that they represented distinctive periods of geological time, an older Cambrian and a younger Silurian, each with their own fossils.

CHECK THESE OUT!

✔FOSSIL ✔GEOLOGIC TIMESCALE ✔ORDOVICIAN PERIOD ✔PALEOZOIC ERA ✔PRECAMBRIAN TIME

Canyon

A deep, narrow, steep-sided valley cut into the surface of the land by a river

Some of the most spectacular features of Earth's surface are deep, narrow, steep-sided valleys called canyons. They are made by fast-flowing rivers down-cutting into the land surface. When the river bed is eroded (worn away) quickly, there is not enough time for the valley sides to be worn down into the wide V-shape typical of other river valleys.

Less well known are submarine (underwater) canyons cut into the submerged edges of the continents. These deep valleys are cut by a type of underwater flow called a turbidity current.

Canyon formation

Canyons are formed mainly in dry and semi-dry regions of the world, such as Mexico and southwest United States. Although rainfall in these regions is uncommon, when the rain does come it is generally very heavy because it is produced by storms. The vast amount of water does not have time to soak into the ground. Instead the water runs off the surface to form trickles of water. These trickles become streams that flow under the influence of gravity into the nearest valley and soon produce raging torrents. The flow of water can be strong enough to carry large boulders and anything else that gets in the way, such as bridges or vehicles.

The heavy rocks carried by the flow rapidly gouge, wear away, and deepen the river bed. When the floodwaters subside (drop), the river may return to being a tiny trickle or even dry out completely—until the next storm when the whole process starts all over again.

Another important part of the process of canyon formation is relief (land surface shape). Rivers flow under the influence of gravity in relation to sea level. High in the mountains, for example, the rivers flow quickly but near sea level they slow down. Canyons such as the Grand Canyon are deeply cut into high plateau landscapes. Rapid down-cutting by their rivers is kept going over a long time by the land being pushed up from within Earth.

The Grand Canyon

Perhaps the most famous canyon in the world is the Grand Canyon in southwest United States. It was first brought to public attention by U.S. explorer John Wesley Powell (1834–1902) in 1869. The magnificence of the canyon has been celebrated over the last 130 years by countless photographers and many poets and artists. Most recently it has been painted and photographed by British artist David Hockney (born 1937).

The canyon winds through the high plateau of parts of Utah, Colorado, Arizona, and New Mexico. Its floor has been cut by the Colorado River to depths of 6,562 feet (2,000 m) in places.

The Grand Canyon has been cut by the Colorado River and winds through southwest United States.

HIGHLIGHTS

◆ Canyons are unusually deep, steep-sided, and narrow valleys.

◆ Canyons are cut into Earth's surface both above and below sea level.

◆ Powerful rivers carrying rock debris cut down through the surface of the land to form canyons.

◆ In the ocean, underwater flows called turbidity currents cut canyons into the submerged edges of the continents.

LOOK CLOSER

Hells Canyon

The deepest canyon in North America is Hells Canyon, 7,900 feet (2,400 m) deep, in the Blue Mountain district of the Columbia Plateau. The canyon runs for 125 miles (200 km) and has been cut by the Snake River. Over millions of years, the river has worn its bed down through a vast pile of Tertiary age volcanic lavas (LAH-vuhz) that stretch across the states of Washington, Oregon, and Idaho for more than 150,000 square miles (390,000 sq km). The whole region has been uplifted by earth movements over the last few millions of years, so the down-cutting power of the river has been maintained. In some places the canyon walls rise almost straight up for thousands of feet. Elsewhere, the layers of lava have worn unevenly into a series of giant steps, each with a different shade of yellow, red, and orange, to produce an amazing colored spectacle.

Apart from its size, the most spectacular features of the Grand Canyon are the different rock strata (STRA-tuh; layers) that form its walls. The sandstone, limestone, and shale layers of strata that make its steep walls tell the story of the early geological history of the western United States from the Permian period (around 286 million to 245 million years ago) to the Cambrian period (around 570 million to 505 million years ago) and beyond to the Precambrian time.

The power of the Colorado River to carry vast amounts of sediment (SEH-duh-muhnt; small particles of material) was shown when the Hoover Dam was built across the river. Lake Mead, which formed behind the dam, soon began to shallow. Engineers discovered that somehow mud was being carried underwater along the whole 62-mile (100-km) length of the lake. They discovered that a new type of underwater flow, called a turbidity current, was responsible. Scientists later realized that the same type of flow had cut submarine canyons.

Submarine canyons

One of the most remarkable discoveries in the oceans of the world is that of the submarine canyons that cut deep into the edges of the continents. These valleys descend from the submerged edges of the continents (around 300 feet or 100 m below sea level) to the ocean floor at depths of around 12,000 feet (4,000 m). Submarine canyons are also cut by turbidity currents. These underwater currents are similar to an avalanche of mud and water mixed together. Turbidity currents can travel for hundreds of miles at speeds of up to 55 miles per hour (89 km/h) and carry vast amounts of sediment onto the ocean floor.

Earthquake tremors often set off the turbidity currents at the top of a canyon. As they flow downward and build up speed, the currents cut down into the canyon floor. When they reach the ocean floor, the currents spread out to form huge fanshaped flows. Eventually they lose speed and deposit (drop) the mud and sand they have been carrying.

CHECK THESE OUT!
✔CLIFF ✔CONTINENTAL SHELF
✔EROSION ✔RIVER
✔VALLEY

Capillary Action

The behavior of liquids in narrow tubes

Water and other liquids do not always behave in the way one would expect. Spilled water does not always make things wet, for example, and sometimes a liquid will climb up a narrow straw against the pull of gravity. This interesting behavior is caused by two related properties, surface tension and capillary action. These properties have a very important effect on the world and on life on Earth.

How surface tension works

The molecules (MAH-lih-KYOOLZ; atoms bonded together) that make up a liquid are in constant motion and exert forces on each other. The forces between the moving molecules allow the liquid to change shape to fit its container but stop the molecules from flying off on their own. Inside a liquid, the forces acting on any molecule pull it equally in all directions because each molecule is surrounded by other molecules.

Water molecules, for example, form hydrogen bonds with their neighbors. Hydrogen bonds are weak. They constantly break and reform as the water molecules move around the liquid. However, hydrogen bonds are vital to hold together the liquid.

The capillary effect in action. Colored water has overcome gravity and been transported to the petals.

The molecules on the surface of a liquid experience a different force because they are being pulled only by the molecules below them or next to them on the surface. There is no balancing outward pull. The result is a force called surface tension that holds in the surface of the liquid and pulls its molecules toward each other. In water, for example, the surface tension is strong enough to allow pond skaters and other insects to walk across water without breaking the surface with their weight.

Because of the force pulling them together, the surface molecules try to get as close together as possible. The ideal shape for a liquid surface is a sphere (ball). However, a liquid's shape is usually distorted by containers and by Earth's gravity. Raindrops and drips from a tap, for example, are teardrop-shaped. The only place to

HIGHLIGHTS

◆ Forces between the molecules in any liquid create a surface tension, pulling the surface inward and together.

◆ Sometimes a liquid can be attracted to its container's surface and will climb up a vertical surface to form a meniscus, which is a curved upper surface.

◆ The narrower a container is, the higher the meniscus can rise.

◆ Capillary action can cause the liquid level to rise considerably in a narrow tube.

see the pure effects of surface tension are in space. Astronauts sometimes demonstrate how, in a gravity-free environment, loose drops of liquid form spinning, wobbling spheres.

Surface tension and capillary action

Surface tension also has important effects when a liquid comes into contact with other materials. The molecules of any other surface will pull on the liquid's surface molecules, fighting against the surface tension and making a droplet of liquid spread out across the surface. The strength of this spreading effect depends on the surface material. For example, a droplet of water will hold together on a wax surface, but on glass it quickly spreads out.

For a material to get wet, the liquid molecules must be more attracted to the surface of the material than they are to each other, so they lose their tendency to hold together. Sometimes the attraction to the surface is strong enough to overcome gravity and a liquid will crawl up a vertical surface of another material. This is called the capillary effect.

Using the capillary effect

In nature, plants use the capillary effect to take water out of the ground and raise it to their leaves and branches. The inside of a plant stem or tree trunk is made of a spongy material called xylem (ZY-luhm). Xylem contains thousands of natural fiber capillary tubes. When water evaporates from the leaves of plants and trees, water is drawn up to replace it. However, the water can only be sucked up a certain distance. The capillary effect helps to transport water upward through the narrow xylem fibers to the tops of trees more than 30 feet (100 m) tall, such as Californian redwoods. The capillary effect is also in action in the earth itself. Water can rise through finely ground soils from an underlying water table (groundwater) to the surface.

Scientists can use capillary action to separate different liquids from mixtures in a chemical laboratory. The capillary can be anything from a glass tube to a piece of absorbent paper with fibers running through it. Because the height that a liquid will rise in a capillary depends on its weight, liquids with different weights will rise to

Capillary Effect

LOOK CLOSER It is easy to see the capillary effect with just a glass of water. At the point where the water meets the glass, the surface of the water curves slightly upward. This curved surface is called a meniscus (muh-NIS-kuhs). A meniscus forms because the molecules of water are attracted to the glass and crowd close to it, pushing up the surface layers so the molecules climb the vertical face of the glass. However, gravity is always pulling back against the water. The attraction of the glass is strong enough to raise only a small weight of water against this pull.

The capillary effect is much more obvious in a narrow, glass capillary tube. Because the weight of the water in a narrow capillary tube can be very small, the capillary effect can sometimes push the water level up by as much as several inches.

The capillary effect can also work in reverse. When a liquid and its container are repelled (not attracted), then a downward-curving meniscus will form, and liquid will push its way toward the bottom of a capillary tube.

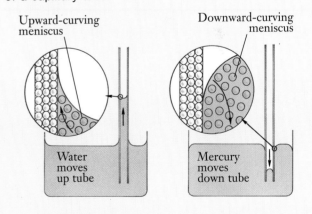

Comparison of the capillary action of water (left) and mercury (right).

different heights in the capillary. This fact is the basis of a science called chromatography (KROH-muh-TAH-gruh-fee), an important way of separating and analyzing chemicals.

CHECK THESE OUT!
✔GRAVITY ✔GROUNDWATER ✔LIQUID
✔SOLID ✔SURFACE TENSION ✔WATER

Carbohydrate

A major class of natural compounds of carbon, hydrogen, and oxygen that includes cellulose, starch, and sugar

When sunlight shines on green plants, carbohydrates are one of the types of molecules that are formed. A chemical compound called chlorophyll (KLOHR-uh-FIL) uses energy from sunlight to change carbon dioxide from the air and water into carbohydrates and oxygen. This process is called photosynthesis (FOH-toh-SIN-thuh-suhs).

The formulas (chemical makeups) of almost all carbohydrates can be written out as $C_x(H_2O)_y$, where x and y are numbers greater than two. This suggested that carbohydrates were compounds of carbon (C) and water (H_2O), or hydrates (the word carbohydrate comes from the term *carbon hydrate*). However, the hydrogen and oxygen in carbohydrates is not in the form of water molecules.

One type of carbohydrate, cellulose (SEL-yuh-LOHS), forms the fibers in wood and other plants. Cellulose is a natural polymer (PAH-luh-muhr; substance made from many identical, small structural units, joined together). It can be used to make paper, plastic film, and textiles. Starches and sugars are also carbohydrates. They are the building blocks of cellulose and also act as energy stores for plants. Carbohydrates are an important food group for humans and other animals. Carbohydrates in the diet provide energy and some of the materials for making cells (SELZ).

Types of sugars

Sugars can be classified (grouped) according to the number of carbon atoms in their chains. Trioses have three carbons, tetroses have four, pentoses have five, hexoses have six, and heptoses have seven carbon atoms in their chains. Most natural sugars, such as glucose, are hexoses.

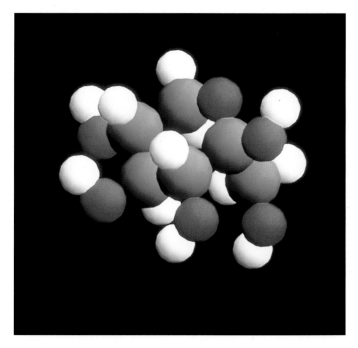

A glucose molecule contains carbon atoms (green), with oxygen (red) and hydrogen (white) atoms.

HIGHLIGHTS

◆ Carbohydrates are compounds of carbon, hydrogen, and oxygen.

◆ Green plants change carbon dioxide and water into carbohydrates and oxygen. This process is called photosynthesis.

◆ Carbohydrates are important sources of energy for humans and other animals.

◆ The general chemical formula for carbohydrates is $C_x(H_2O)_y$.

Porridge oats, bread, potato, rice, pasta, and wheat are all foods rich in complex carbohydrates.

Sugars can also be classified by their chemical structures. Some of the carbon atoms in sugars are linked to hydrogen atoms (-H) and hydroxyl groups (-OH), whereas others are part of carbonyl groups (-CO-). There are two different types of carbonyl groups. If the carbon atom in the carbonyl group is joined to one carbon atom and one hydrogen atom, it is an aldehyde group (C-CO-H). If the carbon atom is connected to two carbon atoms, the carbonyl is a ketone (C-CO-C). Sugars that have an aldehyde group, such as glucose, are called aldoses; sugars with a ketone group, such as fructose, are ketoses:

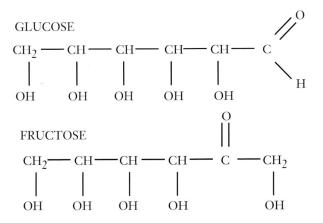

DISCOVERERS

Emil Fischer

German chemist Emil Fischer (1852–1919) spent much of his life teaching chemistry and studying compounds, such as proteins and carbohydrates, that occur in living organisms. Fischer studied the sugars fructose, glucose, and mannose. Each sugar has the chemical formula $C_6H_{12}O_6$, but their atoms are linked together in different ways.

Fischer explored how two of the sugars, glucose and mannose, could have the same chemical formula. He concluded that their atoms are linked together differently around one carbon atom in the molecular chain. The chemical reactions of the two sugars are therefore slightly different, as is the way in which they rotate light.

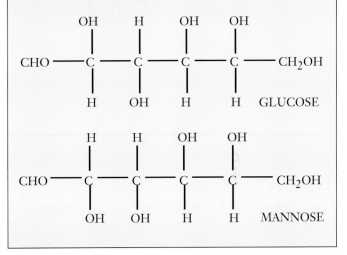

Chains and rings

A hydroxyl group (-OH) in a sugar can react with a carbonyl group (-CO-) to form a linkage through an oxygen atom. If the two reacting groups are part of the same molecule, the reaction forms a ring of atoms. If the hydroxyl group and the carbonyl group are in separate molecules, they react to form a larger molecule.

Sugars are also called saccharides (SA-kuh-RYDZ), from the Greek word *sakcharon*, meaning sugar. Monosaccharides contain only one string of carbon atoms. In solution, that string is an open chain. When monosaccharides crystallize (become crystals), they form rings. Disaccharides contain two strings of carbon atoms linked together by an oxygen atom. Both of the chains

Sugar Structure: Boats and Chairs

Sugar molecules can curl up on themselves and form ring-shaped molecules when two parts of the same molecule react together. This happens when sugars solidify (become solid). Although the rings in sugars are often shown as being flat, in reality they tend to form one of two shapes. In one form called the chair configuration, alternate atoms are above and below the centerline of the ring. In the other form called the boat configuration, four atoms in the ring lie in a flat plane while the other two lie above that plane. Different sugars have either one form or the other, depending on the sizes of the groups of atoms that are attached to the ring atoms. Sugars that form rings with five atoms can also have different shapes. The ring can twist one way or the other, depending on the groups of atoms attached to the ring atoms.

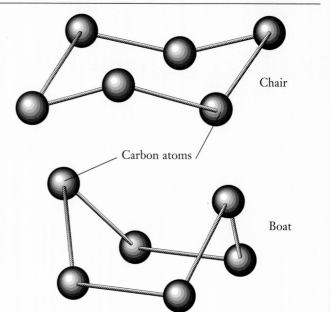

Chair

Carbon atoms

Boat

can form rings by the reaction between a hydroxy group and a carbonyl group. Sucrose is the sugar used to sweeten drinks and food. It is made of one glucose and one fructose molecule. The two parts are joined by an oxygen atom, and each is curled into a ring in crystals of sugar.

Polysaccharides
Polysaccharides are long molecules that form when many monosaccharide units join together. Many natural fibers and tissues are types of polysaccharides. Cellulose is a polysaccharide that is contained in the cell walls of plants. It contains as many as 15,000 monosaccharide units joined in long chains. These molecules do not dissolve in water because they are so large.

The disaccharide sucrose consists of glucose (left) and fructose (right) linked by oxygen.

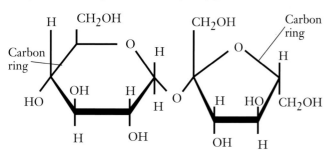

Starches contain hundreds of monosaccharide units in each molecule. Starches are used to treat fabrics, as thickeners for foods, and as the basis of adhesives (glues). Glycogen contains many thousands of monosaccharide units. Living organisms use glycogen as a source of energy.

Rotation of light
When light is shone through a polarizing film of the type used in certain sunglasses, part of the light is blocked by the film. The part of the light that passes through the filter will normally only pass through a second sheet of polarizing film if that film polarizes in the same direction.

In the 19th century, scientists discovered that sugar solutions could change the polarization of light. If a test tube containing a sugar solution is placed between two polarizing filters, the second filter has to be turned through an angle for light to shine through it. The size and direction of the angle depend on the type of sugar used. If the second filter has to be turned clockwise in the direction of the light beam, the sugar, for example glucose, is called D-glucose. L-glucose turns light counterclockwise.

CHECK THESE OUT!
✔CARBON ✔ISOMER ✔ORGANIC CHEMISTRY

Carbon

A nonmetallic element that forms millions of compounds, many of which are essential to life on Earth

Charcoal has a high carbon content and is produced by burning wood without oxygen.

Few people would connect bright, sparkling diamonds with dull, black coal. Yet both are made of the element carbon (chemical symbol C). Carbon is one of the small number of elements (substances with similar atoms) found in a pure form in nature. It also forms millions of compounds with other elements. Compounds in which carbon atoms are bonded to hydrogen atoms and (possibly) atoms of other elements are called organic carbon compounds. Carbon compounds not containing carbon-hydrogen bonds, such as the mineral limestone (calcium carbonate), are usually called inorganic. Chemists once thought that only living organisms could produce organic compounds. This idea was mistaken, and chemists are now able to make all organic compounds from a few inorganic carbon-containing compounds.

Carbon has two main oxides. Carbon dioxide (CO_2) is produced by breathing animals and used by growing plants. Carbon monoxide (CO) is extremely poisonous to warm-blooded animals, including humans.

HIGHLIGHTS

♦ Carbon is a nonmetallic element found naturally as diamond and graphite.

♦ Carbon can make a huge number of organic or inorganic compounds with other elements, either naturally or artificially.

♦ Carbon is the only element that can form a variety of long chains and rings of its atoms.

♦ Coal is an impure form of carbon that is mined in many parts of the world.

Carbon is the lightest member of group 14 (IVA) of the periodic table, which groups elements according to their chemical properties and increasing atomic weight. The atomic mass of carbon is approximately 12. Carbon atoms normally form four bonds with other atoms. The bond between a pair of atoms can be single, double, or triple, meaning that the carbon atom and its partner in the bond are held together by one, two, or three linkages.

The main isotope (EYE-suh-TOHP; type) of carbon is carbon 12, which makes up nearly 99 percent of all carbon atoms. The nucleus (NOO-klee-uhs; center) of a carbon 12 atom has six protons (positively charged particles) and six neutrons (uncharged particles). Carbon 12 is by international agreement taken to be the basis of the atomic mass scale, so the atomic mass of pure carbon 12 is exactly 12.00. Carbon 13 makes up just over one percent of carbon atoms. Carbon 13 has an extra neutron in its nucleus. Tiny amounts of radioactive carbon 14, with two extra neutrons, are made when radiation from space hits nitrogen atoms in the atmosphere.

Forms of carbon

Two forms of pure carbon are found in nature, graphite (GRA-fyt) and diamond. Graphite is a shiny gray-black solid mined in Madagascar, Mexico, and Sri Lanka, among other places. Graphite can also be made by heating petroleum coke to high temperatures (petroleum coke is a by-product of oil refining). Diamond is mined from underground shafts of volcanic rock in South Africa and Brazil. Most diamonds are transparent and colorless. Some diamonds are colored by the presence of tiny amounts of other elements. Typical colors are blue and black, but yellow and pink diamonds are sometimes found.

Coal is an impure form of carbon formed by the fossilization (preservation) of plant matter. The carbon level in coal depends on the type of coal. Anthracite (AN-thruh-syt), for example, contains around 87 percent carbon. Coke is a form of carbon made by heating coal to remove some impurities. Coke is used as a source of carbon in many industrial processes, including iron and steel manufacture. Oil and natural gas contain carbon in combination with hydrogen and smaller amounts of nitrogen and sulfur.

Organic chemicals

Organic chemicals are substances that contain from one to hundreds of thousands of carbon

---

LOOK CLOSER

Structure and Bonding in Carbon

Every carbon atom forms four bonds (links) to its neighboring atoms. These bonds take a number of different forms. In diamond, for example, each carbon atom is surrounded by four other carbon atoms. These atoms form the shape of a tetrahedron, a triangular-based pyramid. Because each of the surrounding carbon atoms is connected to three more carbon atoms and so on, a diamond is a single enormous molecule (a macromolecule). The atoms in diamond are so tightly bound together that diamond is the hardest substance known.

Graphite has a very different structure from that of diamond. The carbon atoms in graphite are arranged in honeycomblike sheets. Each carbon atom has three close neighbors with which it forms single bonds. The fourth bond is shared equally between all three neighboring atoms. Because this fourth bond is not tied to one particular pair of atoms, it is said to be delocalized. The sheets of carbon atoms in graphite form a stack. However, since there is no bonding between the sheets, only a weak attraction, the sheets can easily slide over each other. It is this property that makes graphite useful for making pencil leads. As a pencil moves over paper, the sheets of graphite slide off the stack and leave a gray-black trace of carbon on the surface of the paper. Graphite is also used as a lubricant (LOO-brih-kuhnt; substance that prevents friction) because its sheets of carbon atoms slide over each other so easily.

A third form of carbon has the formula C_{60} and is called buckminsterfullerene (BUHK-MIHN-stuhr-FOO-luh-REEN). This compound is so named because its molecules look like the domes designed by U.S. engineer Buckminster Fuller (1895–1983).

In a way, buckminsterfullerene is similar to a graphite sheet that has curled up on itself. Each carbon atom in a C_{60} molecule has single bonds with three immediate neighbors and a fourth bond that it shares between those neighbors. Buckminsterfullerene has been made artificially and is believed to be a major part of soot. Other ball-shaped carbon molecules have been made with 70 or more carbon atoms. The general name given to these molecules is fullerene.

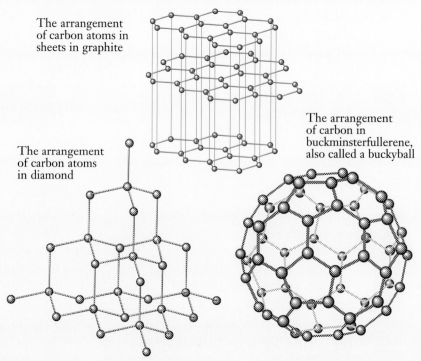

The arrangement of carbon atoms in sheets in graphite

The arrangement of carbon in buckminsterfullerene, also called a buckyball

The arrangement of carbon atoms in diamond

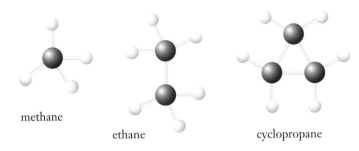

methane

ethane

cyclopropane

Carbon is a unique element. Carbon atoms are able to join together in long chains. Chains of carbon atoms can join up into rings.

atoms in each molecule. Organic chemicals normally contain hydrogen and sometimes other elements such as nitrogen, oxygen, and sulfur. Scientists named these substances *organic* because the first organic chemicals to be studied were taken from living organisms.

The range of organic compounds is enormous for three reasons. First, carbon is the only element that can form long chains and rings of its atoms. Second, carbon can form links with a wide variety of other elements. Third, the possibility of single, double, and triple bonds between carbon atoms and with atoms of other elements adds to the range of options for joining atoms to make molecules.

Methane is the simplest organic compound. Its formula is CH_4 and it has a tetrahedral (four-faced) shape with four hydrogen atoms clustered around a carbon atom. Methane is the main component of natural gas. Ethane has the formula C_2H_6. Its two carbon atoms are linked by a single bond. Each carbon atom is attached to three hydrogen atoms.

The simplest ring compound is cyclopropane (C_3H_6), which has a triangle of bonds between its three carbon atoms. Each carbon atom is also connected to two hydrogen atoms.

Inorganic carbon compounds

Not all compounds of carbon are organic. The oxides carbon monoxide (CO) and carbon dioxide (CO_2) are formed when carbon compounds burn. Carbon dioxide is also produced by animal respiration. Carbon dioxide dissolves in water to form carbonic acid, H_2CO_3. Many metals form salts of this acid, such as magnesium carbonate, $MgCO_3$. Silicon carbide

EVERYDAY SCIENCE

Diamonds

In 1990, the journal *Science* chose diamond as its Molecule of the Year because of its outstanding properties. The unique structure of diamond makes it extremely resistant to attack by chemicals and radiation. Diamond is an excellent heat conductor and is extremely hard and transparent (see-through). The properties of hardness and transparency make diamonds valuable for making and cutting tools and jewelry. Because of the market value of diamonds, it is not surprising that people have been trying to make diamonds from graphite ever since 1797, when it was discovered that both diamond and graphite are forms of the same element, carbon. It took more than 150 years for anyone to succeed in making diamonds. On February 16, 1955, the General Electric Company (GEC) announced that researchers in its laboratories had managed to make diamonds from graphite. The team at GEC used temperatures over 5100°F (2800°C) and pressures more than 100,000 times the normal pressure at Earth's surface. In nature, diamonds form under similar conditions in hot, molten rocks deep under Earth's surface. The diamonds made by the GEC team were small and dull. They were made to be used as hard teeth in cutting tools. More recently, diamonds as large as ⅓ inch (8 mm) have been made. It seems unlikely that diamonds suitable for making jewelry will be made in the near future. Industrially made diamonds are not attractive enough because they are not clear and do not sparkle.

(SiC) and carbon disulfide (CS_2) are further examples of inorganic carbon compounds.

CHECK THESE OUT!

✔CARBON DIOXIDE ✔COAL ✔HYDROCARBON
✔IRON AND STEEL ✔LIMESTONE ✔ORGANIC CHEMISTRY

Carbon Dioxide

An odorless, invisible gas

Carbon dioxide is important for life on Earth. It helps to keep Earth's climate warm enough for living organisms to survive, and it is vital for the growth of plants. Carbon dioxide is familiar as the bubbles in carbonated soft drinks and as the dry ice that is used to chill food and for special effects in movies and the theater. It is also used in fire extinguishers. At room temperature, carbon dioxide is a colorless, odorless gas that is heavier than air. Its chemical formula is CO_2.

Carbon dioxide does not burn or support burning, which is why it is used in fire extinguishers. It dissolves in water to make a slightly acidic solution called carbonic acid. Carbon dioxide dissolves under pressure. When

HIGHLIGHTS

♦ Carbon dioxide is a colorless, odorless gas at room temperature.

♦ Under pressure, carbon dioxide dissolves in water; when the pressure is released, carbon dioxide gas bubbles out again.

♦ Carbon dioxide is a greenhouse gas, produced by burning fossil fuels such as oil products and coal.

♦ Carbon dioxide plays an important part in the life cycles of plants and animals.

A molecule of carbon dioxide (CO_2) has one atom of carbon joined to two oxygen atoms.

EVERYDAY SCIENCE

Chilling with CO_2

When solid carbon dioxide, or dry ice, reaches –110°F (–79°C), it starts to turn into cold carbon dioxide gas. This chills the air around it and produces a heavy fog that clings to the ground and is often seen as a theatrical effect in films and stage shows. Dry ice also has practical uses. The chilling effect caused by carbon dioxide turning from solid to gas can be used to keep things cool. A refrigerated railroad car can be kept cool long enough to carry food from California to New York using 1,000 pounds (454 kg) of dry ice. At the end of the journey, most of the carbon dioxide would have evaporated and left the car. It would take 10 times as much normal ice to produce the same cooling effect. Also, the melting water would have to be drained off to prevent rust.

the pressure is released, the gas bubbles out of solution. This effect causes the bubbles that appear when a soft-drink bottle is opened.

Carbon dioxide has an unusual property: it does not become a liquid at normal pressure. Instead, solid carbon dioxide turns directly to gas at temperatures above –110°F (–79°C). This process is called sublimation.

Animal respiration (using oxygen to release energy from food) and fuel burning are two major sources of carbon dioxide in the atmosphere. About 0.04 percent of Earth's atmosphere is carbon dioxide. Carbon dioxide can be purified from air by cooling the air until solid carbon dioxide forms. Carbon dioxide can be used as solid blocks or stored in gas cylinders.

Carbon dioxide can be produced by adding acid to metal carbonates and bicarbonates or to hydrogen carbonates. The gas can be trapped in a balloon or in a glass jar that is first filled with water, then held with its mouth under water. Carbon dioxide is also produced by burning fuels and by the fermentation of sugar by yeast.

Carbon dioxide takes part in relatively few chemical reactions. It reacts with the oxides and hydroxides of certain metals to form carbonates and bicarbonates. Hot carbon or zinc can change carbon dioxide into carbon monoxide (CO).

Respiration and photosynthesis

Carbon dioxide plays an important part in the life cycles of all living organisms, but most obviously plants and animals. Humans and other animals inhale oxygen from the air. They use this oxygen to burn up food and provide energy for life. Burning up food produces carbon dioxide, which is exhaled (breathed out) to the atmosphere through lungs or gills.

Plants take in carbon dioxide through their leaves as part of a process called photosynthesis (FOH-toh-SIN-thuh-suhs). When the Sun shines on a plant, a green substance called chlorophyll (KLOHR-uh-FIL) changes carbon dioxide and water into oxygen and materials such as simple sugars, which are needed for plant growth. The oxygen formed by photosynthesis is released to the atmosphere. The balance between photosynthesis and respiration is important. Photosynthesis in plants produces oxygen that helps support most living organisms. Respiration in most living organisms produces carbon dioxide that supports plant life.

Global warming

The glass in a greenhouse warms the plants and soil inside by letting sunlight in and trapping the heat that is produced by the sunlight. Carbon dioxide keeps Earth's atmosphere warm by absorbing the heat that is radiated by Earth's surface and preventing it from escaping into space. Other gases, such as methane, have a similar effect. The amount of warming depends on the concentration of carbon dioxide in the atmosphere. The balance of respiration and photosynthesis helps to keep this concentration stable. Large amounts of extra carbon dioxide are being produced by burning fossil fuels, such as oil products and coal. Scientists are concerned that the additional carbon dioxide being produced will cause Earth to overheat. This could cause drastic changes in Earth's climate such as drought, storms, and flooding.

CHECK THESE OUT!
✔CARBON ✔CAVE ✔CHEMICAL REACTION
✔CHEMISTRY ✔GLOBAL WARMING

LOOK CLOSER

Stalactites and Stalagmites

Stalactites (stuh-LAK-TYTS) and stalagmites (stuh-LAG-MYTS) are a feature of many caves. They form when rainwater trickles through rocks that contain calcium, such as limestone, and then drips from the roof of a cave. Carbon dioxide in rainwater combines with calcium salts in rocks to form calcium bicarbonate. This salt dissolves in rainwater, and the solution trickles through cracks in the rock. When rainwater enters a cave, some of the carbon dioxide present in the water evaporates. This process turns calcium bicarbonate into calcium carbonate, which does not dissolve in water. The calcium carbonate becomes solid at this point and gradually builds up to form a stalactite where the rainwater breaks through the roof of the cave. Another build-up, called a stalagmite, forms where the rainwater drips onto the floor. Although calcium carbonate is white, other minerals dissolved in the rainwater can produce streaks of color in stalactites and stalagmites. Over time, stalactites and stalagmites can meet up to form columns that join the roof to the floor.

Caribbean Sea

Area off the east coast of Central America containing the Caribbean islands

To travelers everywhere the Caribbean means sandy beaches, coral reefs, and clear blue water. Beneath the peaceful surface, however, the region was formed by powerful forces. Millions of years ago the Caribbean Sea was created by movements of the giant tectonic plates that make up Earth's crust.

Geography of the Caribbean

The Caribbean Sea is a roughly oval basin edged by Central America to the west and by the South American countries of Colombia and Venezuela to the south. To the east, a curved string of islands stretch from Trinidad to Cuba. These Caribbean islands, also called the West Indies, separate the Caribbean Sea from the Atlantic Ocean. The northern islands, including Cuba, Jamaica, and Puerto Rico, form an island chain

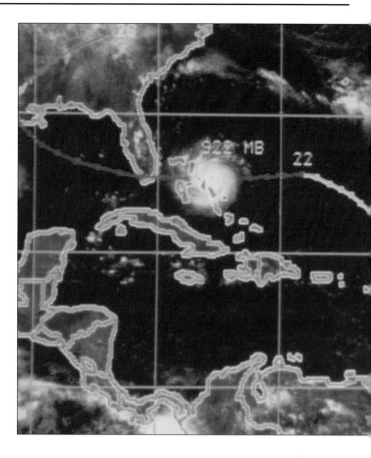

Hurricane Andrew, shown as a white swirl, approaching Cuba and Florida in August 1992.

called the Greater Antilles. The Lesser Antilles are the southern chain, which includes the Virgin Islands, Trinidad, and Tobago. Most Caribbean islands are formed of coral limestone.

The Caribbean Sea measures 1,020,000 square miles (2,640,000 sq km). The water is no deeper than 25,216 feet (7,685 m). The sea is made up of five basins separated by undersea ridges. From west to east, they are the Yucatán, Cayman, Colombian, Venezuelan, and Grenada basins.

Origins of the Caribbean

Scientists believe that millions of years ago the Caribbean region was close to the Mediterranean Sea. Around 110 million years ago, during the Mesozoic (MEH-zuh-ZOH-ik) era, the plates on which the two seas rested slowly began to pull apart, forming the Atlantic Ocean.

Plate movement heats up the rocks beneath the crust. Eventually the rocks melt and rise to the surface, erupting as lava (LAH-vuh). Five million years ago volcanic eruptions like this formed the Lesser Antilles. Plate activity is still

---

HIGHLIGHTS

◆ The Caribbean Sea measures over one million square miles (2,640,000 sq km). The deepest water is about 25,216 feet (7,685 m) deep.

◆ The Caribbean Sea is an oval basin edged by Central and South America to the west and south, and to the east by a curved string of islands stretching from Trinidad to Cuba.

◆ Millions of years ago the Caribbean Sea was formed by movement of the huge tectonic plates that make up Earth's crust. Plate movement caused, and still causes, earthquakes and volcanic activity in the region.

happening. In 1997, a volcano on Montserrat, an island in the chain, erupted. Plate movement also causes earthquakes in the region.

Scientists once thought that the Caribbean basin lay on either the North American or the South American plates. However, new studies show that the area has its own plate, one of about 20 in the world. Scientists have also discovered that the Caribbean plate is moving eastward, while the North and South American plates are moving westward. Earthquakes and volcanic activity in the region are set to continue.

Climate

Winds, water currents, and height above sea level all affect the climate of the Caribbean islands. Rainfall varies greatly between the islands. For example, the island of Bonaire in the Lesser Antilles receives only 10 inches (25 cm) of rain each year. Parts of the large island of Dominica receive 350 inches (889 cm) of rain each year.

Between June and November violent storms called hurricanes often affect the islands. Early in the season, hurricanes develop in the Caribbean and the Gulf of Mexico as the shallow water gets warmer. Areas of low pressure to the north often push these storms into the Gulf of Mexico. Later in the summer as the Atlantic Ocean gets warmer, the hurricanes move mainly to the east. In autumn they return to the Caribbean as the ocean begins to cool again.

Coral reefs

Coral reefs are a huge Caribbean attraction. These large but delicate structures are made from the skeletons of millions of tiny creatures called coral polyps (PAH-luhps), held together by algae (AL-jee; plantlike

Tourists can cause great damage to the coral reefs.

organisms). Coral polyps grow best just a few feet below the sea surface, where they receive plenty of oxygen and sunlight. Coral reefs attract many different kinds of fish, including barracudas, marlins, and groupers. Rare sea turtles, manta rays, spiny lobsters, and marine mammals such as dolphins and manatees also flourish in the Caribbean.

Threats to the reefs

Tourism is one of the most important industries in the Caribbean. Scuba diving and fishing among the reefs bring much-needed cash to the islands. Overfishing and tourist development, however, have caused great damage to the reefs.

Coral reefs need clear water and plenty of fish to control the growth of algae. Recently the waters of the Caribbean have become clouded by sand washed from the beaches. The beaches have been disturbed because new resorts have been built. Floating sand blocks the sunlight the coral polyps need to grow.

Tourism also adds to sewage levels in the water. Minerals used in farming, such as fertilizers, are also washed out to sea. The waste and minerals encourage the growth of a type of algae that kills the coral. In the past, algae-eating fish have controlled the growth of these algae, but overfishing has greatly reduced the numbers of these useful fish.

CHECK THESE OUT!
✔ATLANTIC OCEAN
✔CLIMATE
✔ISLAND
✔PLATE TECTONICS

Catalyst

A substance that changes the rate of a chemical reaction without itself being changed in any way

Around one sixth of all the goods produced in the United States involve the use of catalysts (KA-tuhl-uhsts). Catalysts are substances that change the rate of a chemical reaction without themselves being changed. Not all catalysts are used in industry, however. Catalysts called enzymes are very important in living organisms. In the human body, enzymes help to change food into new tissue and release the energy that makes people's lungs breathe and their hearts beat. Other enzymes, such as those produced by yeast, are essential in brewing and baking. Catalysts were named in 1835 by Swedish chemist Jöns Jakob Berzelius (1779–1848), but they had been used for many years before that.

How catalysts work

In a chemical reaction, one set of substances (the reactants) is broken up and rearranged to form a new set of substances (the products). The reactant molecules (MAH-lih-KYOOLZ; atoms bonded together) are held together by chemical bonds. Chemical reactions usually take place in a series of steps. Each step involves

HIGHLIGHTS

◆ Catalysts are substances that allow a chemical reaction to take place at faster rate or at a lower temperature than is otherwise possible.

◆ A catalyst does not change chemically as a result of the reaction and can often be reused.

◆ Catalysts have an extremely important role in many industrial processes.

◆ Enzymes are catalysts that help in the chemical breakdown of food.

the making or breaking of one or two bonds. In many cases the step will not occur unless the molecular pieces come together with more than a certain amount of energy. The step that requires the most energy is called the rate-determining step. The energy required is called the activation energy for the reaction.

Sometimes the activation energy is so great that a reaction will happen too slowly to be of any practical use. The reactants may have to be heated to a high temperature, which could make the reaction too expensive to turn into a commercial process. A catalyst, however, can take part in the rate-determining step in such a way that it lowers the activation energy and yet is released unchanged at the end of the reaction. Alternatively, the catalyst might provide another path by which the same products can be produced. Therefore a

A large wire gauze, the catalyst for making nitric acid. Nitric acid is made into fertilizers.

reaction that might normally take weeks to complete could take just a few hours or minutes with a catalyst, which could make it commercially useful. By reducing the activation energy, a catalyst speeds up the rate of a chemical reaction but does not increase the amount of products that are formed. Unlike the reactants, the catalyst itself remains chemically the same at the end of the process. Usually only a very small amount of the catalyst is needed, and it can often be reused.

Types of catalysts

A different catalyst is usually needed for each different reaction, although some catalysts work with numerous different reactions. Some catalysts are solids, others are liquids or gases. A catalyst may be in the same physical state (phase) as the reactants. For example, both the reactants and the catalyst may be liquids. Sometimes the catalyst is a solid and the reactants are gases. A solid catalyst speeds up reactions between gases by allowing the gases to react more quickly on its solid surface, which acts like a kind of worktable.

Not all catalysts speed up a chemical reaction. Negative catalysts slow down a reaction or prevent it from continuing by interfering with the way the reactants are changed into products. A reaction can also be slowed down in other ways. Sometimes impurities poison a catalyst and stop it from working. For example, platinum catalysts used in catalytic converters to purify automobile exhausts are poisoned by lead. Only unleaded gasoline can therefore be used in automobiles that have catalytic converters. Although a catalyst remains chemically unchanged during a reaction, if it is gradually poisoned by impurities it has to be replaced.

Catalysts in action

Many industrial processes depend on catalysts, such as the Haber process in which ammonia (NH_3; used to make fertilizer, among other things) is produced from hydrogen (H_2) and nitrogen (N_2):

$$3H_2 + N_2 \rightarrow 2NH_3$$

Normally this reaction happens very slowly and only under high pressure, but adding an iron catalyst (with traces of other metals) speeds it up. The iron provides a surface on which the

LOOK CLOSER

Converters

Catalytic converters have been fitted to most U.S. automobiles since the mid-1970s and help reduce the effects of smog (smoke and fog) in polluted cities. Catalytic converters work by changing the harmful gases in automobile exhausts into other, less harmful gases. Hydrocarbons (unburned fuel made up of hydrogen and carbon) are changed into water and carbon dioxide, and nitrogen oxide is changed into nitrogen and oxygen. Inside a catalytic converter there is a catalyst made of platinum and palladium metals. These metals are coated onto a honeycomb structure to provide the maximum surface area over which the chemical reactions can take place. Although catalytic converters are very effective, reducing harmful gases by around 90 percent, they can be used only with unleaded fuel. Also, they work only when the engine has warmed the exhaust gases to a high temperature.

Nitrogen, oxygen, carbon dioxide, and water

Hydrocarbons and nitrogen oxide

hydrogen and nitrogen molecules can split into their individual atoms. One nitrogen atom then combines with three hydrogen atoms to make a single molecule of ammonia gas. The ammonia escapes from the surface of the catalyst, leaving it free for other molecules to react on.

Enzymes are proteins that act as catalysts inside living organisms, speeding up the chemical reactions on which all life depends. An enzyme called pepsin, for example, helps people to digest meat, eggs, and other substances much more rapidly. Fermentation (the process of turning sugar into alcohol and carbon dioxide) is perhaps the best known use of enzymes. Yeast produces an enzyme that causes the fermentation.

CHECK THESE OUT!

✔CHEMICAL REACTION ✔ENERGY ✔PETROCHEMICAL

Cathode Ray

Beam of electrons that is used to draw the picture in television sets and oscilloscopes

Televisions, computer monitors, radar sets, and oscilloscopes (ah-SIH-luh-SKOHPS; scientific instruments that draw graphs on small television screens) were originally based on an electronic device called a cathode-ray tube. In this long glass tube, a beam of rays from a heated electrical terminal (called a cathode) at one end is shot onto a fluorescent (floo-REH-suhnt; glowing) screen at the other. An image such as a television picture can be built up on the screen by bending (deflecting) the beam.

Cathode rays were first discovered in the 19th century by German and British physicists. They found that cathode rays are beams of electrons, or negatively charged particles normally found circling the nucleus (NOO-klee-uhs; center) of every atom, that travel at high speed. Soon afterward the cathode-ray tube was built. The best known cathode-ray tube is the picture tube used in television sets. Only recently has the cathode-ray tube begun to be replaced by semiconductor or liquid crystal displays for portable devices such as laptop computers.

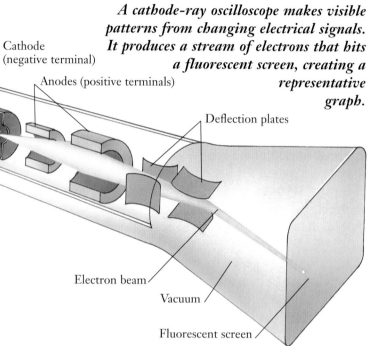

A cathode-ray oscilloscope makes visible patterns from changing electrical signals. It produces a stream of electrons that hits a fluorescent screen, creating a representative graph.

Cathode (negative terminal)

Anodes (positive terminals)

Deflection plates

Electron beam

Vacuum

Fluorescent screen

HIGHLIGHTS

◆ Cathode rays are beams of tiny, negatively charged particles of matter called electrons traveling at very high speeds.

◆ Cathode-ray tubes direct a stream of electrons onto a screen where an image is formed.

◆ Computer monitors, television sets, and radar sets are examples of machines that contain cathode-ray tubes.

Discovery of cathode rays

Early experiments with cathode rays used gas discharge tubes similar to those used in street lamps and neon signs. These long glass bulbs contain a positive terminal (anode) and a negative terminal (cathode). When a high voltage is connected across the two terminals, an electrical current or discharge flows from the cathode to the anode. If the air is removed from the tube and replaced with a gas such as neon, the tube glows when the current flows.

In 1858, German mathematician Julius Plücker (1801–1868) experimented with a gas discharge tube filled with air. As he pumped the air out to create a vacuum (VA-kyoom; empty space), he found that a current flowed from the cathode to the anode, making the wall of the tube near the anode glow green. Plücker was able to move the glowing spot around the tube by placing a magnet nearby. German physicist Eugen Goldstein (1850–1930) showed that an obstacle placed in the path of the rays cast a shadow on the wall of the tube. Goldstein found he too could bend the rays with a magnet. He concluded that the rays were negatively charged particles and he called them cathode rays. British physicist Sir William Crookes (1832–1919) built an early form of cathode-ray tube in 1880.

Discovery of the electron

In 1897, British physicist J. J. Thomson (1856–1940) used an improved gas discharge tube from which almost all the air had been removed to carry out more accurate experiments. He showed that the cathode-ray beam could be bent by an electric field (the force field created by an electric charge) and a magnetic field. Thomson measured the charge and mass (amount of matter) of the particles in cathode rays by changing the strength of the electric field and watching how much the beam was bent. Using different gases in the discharge tube, such as air, hydrogen, and carbon dioxide, he always got the same result. He said that cathode rays are made up of negatively charged corpuscles (now called electrons) present in every kind of atom. These experiments inspired him to put forward his plum-pudding theory of the atom. This theory suggested that atoms had tiny negative electrons embedded like plums in a pudding of positively charged matter. However, British physicist Ernest Rutherford (1871–1937) proved that electrons move around the nucleus.

Television sets contain a cathode-ray tube. The image is beamed to the screen at the front.

LOOK CLOSER

Oscilloscopes

An oscilloscope or cathode-ray oscilloscope is similar to a small television set that can draw graphs of electrical signals. It is based around a cathode-ray tube whose screen is calibrated (marked out) with squares like those on graph paper. The picture in a television set is built up of dots formed as the cathode-ray beam scans across a phosphor screen. In an oscilloscope the picture is formed in a different way. One electrical signal (called x) is connected to a set of electrical plates that move the beam from left to right. Another signal (called y) is connected to plates that move the beam up and down. As the x and y signals change, the cathode-ray beam plots a graph on the screen just as people draw graphs by plotting values of x and y on graph paper. The best-known use of the oscilloscope is in electronic heart monitors (electrocardiographs), which show heartbeats as regular pulses on a screen.

Cathode-ray tubes

The cathode-ray tube was invented in 1897 by German physicist Karl Ferdinand Braun (1850–1918). This long glass vacuum tube has a cathode at one end and a wide fluorescent screen at the other. When heated, a cathode gives off a beam of negatively charged cathode rays. Because unlike charges attract, these rays are pulled along quickly by a positive terminal (anode) halfway down the tube. The rays travel so fast that they shoot past the anode and hit the screen. The screen is coated with phosphor (FAHS-fuhr), a material that glows when the cathode rays hit it.

In a television set, electromagnets (magnets with a field strength created by an electrical current) inside the tube focus and deflect (bend) the cathode-ray beam. The glowing spot can therefore be moved up and down and from side to side around the screen in a process called scanning. When the beam moves quickly enough, an image such as a television picture can be built up.

CHECK THESE OUT!
✔ATOM ✔ELECTRON ✔LUMINESCENCE

Cave

A naturally formed opening into Earth's surface that may continue deep underground

Many creatures hide in caves to protect themselves from the heat, the cold, the wind and rain, and from the darkness and the light. Some animals also live in caves to protect themselves from predators, to store food, or as bases for hunting.

Caves are openings in the ground surface, both above and below sea level. They can be formed by many different natural processes including rivers, glaciers (GLAY-shuhrz; large bodies of ice), and lava (LAH-vuh) flows. However, caves are found only where the right mixture of natural processes and certain rock types occur. The most common caves are those formed underground when the lime in the rock is chemically altered to bicarbonate of lime. This form of lime dissolves in water. Gradually the limestone disappears, leaving behind a cave.

A cave may be a single relatively large and easily reached opening in the rocks, such as a coastal sea cave or cliff-base rock shelter. Elsewhere, for example in limestone areas, cave systems may extend for hundreds of miles underground. The size of a cave is limited only by the strength of the rock walls that support its roof. The biggest single cave chamber in the world is Lubang Nasib Bagus in Sarawak, on one of the Malaysian islands. This chamber is 2,300 feet (700 m) long, up to 1,300 feet (400 m) wide, and 230 feet (70 m) high.

Age of caves

The formation of caves can be very difficult to date as there is no direct way of telling when a cave first began to form. Some caves contain deposits of minerals, sediment (SEH-duh-muhnt; small particles of material), fossils (FAH-suhlz; preserved evidence of past life), human artwork, tools,

HIGHLIGHTS

♦ Most caves are formed in limestone landscapes. The lime chemically changes to form bicarbonate of lime, which dissolves in water to leave a space.

♦ Other types of caves include lava caves, glacier and ice caves, sea caves, and sandstone caves.

♦ Many caves contain characteristic features such as stalactites and stalagmites.

♦ The presence of fossils and cave art show that many living organisms, including human ancestors, have sheltered in caves for thousands of years.

and weapons. Sometimes these items can be dated in one of two main ways. Measurement of radioactive decay of certain mineral elements gives the date the mineral first formed. For example, bones and charcoal can be dated from their carbon isotopes (EYE-suh-TOHPS; variations in the atoms of an element), but only as far back as 45,000 years ago. Stalactites (stuh-LAK-TYTS; mineral growths from cave roofs or walls) up to 350,000 years old can be dated using radioactive isotopes of the elements uranium and thorium. Fossil identification in cave sediments can reveal when the deposits took place because living organisms have evolved through time. Many caves have developed over the last 10,000 years or so since the last glacial retreat of the recent ice age. Most older

A lava tube, made when a shell of lava solidified while the liquid center flowed away.

cave systems have been removed by weathering and erosion. However, hot and wet tropical regions such as Sarawak in Malaysia, which has some of the largest caves in the world, did not experience the ice age. These limestone caves are two million years old or more.

Ancient limestones formed landscapes many millions of years ago and contain fossil caves and fissures (FIH-shuhrz; cracks). Carboniferous limestones (deposited around 340 million years ago) in southwest England and South Wales in Great Britain formed landscapes with caves in late Triassic times, around 210 million years ago. Scientists know these caves and fissures formed then because they contain Triassic sediments and fossils, some from the earliest mammals.

Limestone caves

Most caves are formed in limestone landscapes, although many other geological circumstances can produce cavelike openings in the ground surface. These openings include lava tubes, ice and glacial caves, sea caves, and sandstone caves.

The development of cave systems in limestone landscapes results from the chemistry of limestone rock. Limestone rock is largely calcium carbonate, sometimes formed by the piling up of vast layers of shells and skeletons of sea-dwelling creatures such as corals and clams. Compressed

Limestone caves begin to form when weakly acidic groundwater moves underground through a swallow hole and into fissures, faults, and joints.

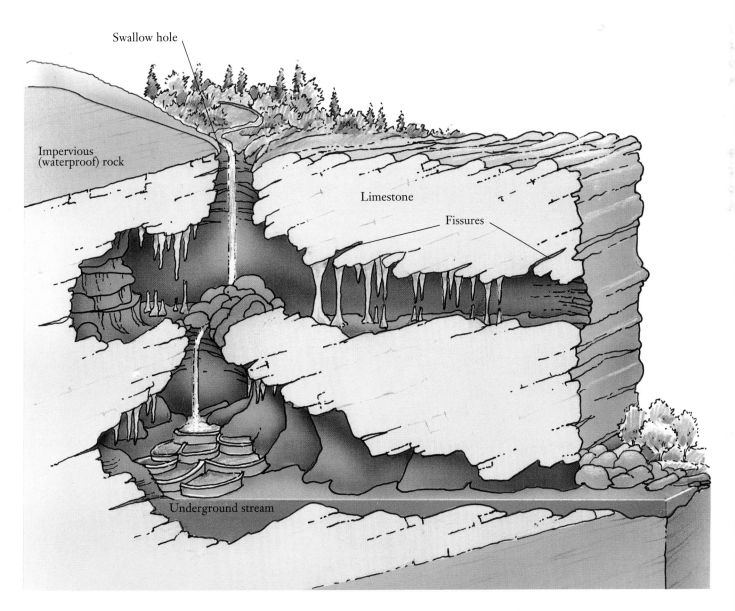

Swallow hole

Impervious (waterproof) rock

Limestone

Fissures

Underground stream

into limestone rock and uplifted by movements of the earth, limestones are weathered and eroded like any other rock. They can be dissolved slowly by rainwater containing carbon dioxide from the atmosphere, which together form the weakly acidic carbonic acid. The limestone goes into solution as calcium bicarbonate. Rainwater running over limestone slowly dissolves the rock. As most limestones are fairly brittle rocks, their strata (STRAH-tuh; layers) are broken into blocks with vertical fissures. Rainwater seeps through these cracks.

The fissures and underground flow channels enlarge as their walls are dissolved. The pattern of underground channel flow and the resulting cave system is often controlled by the pattern of geological joints in the area. One example is the cave system of the Black Hills of South Dakota. Channel enlargement can make the rock roof collapse in places and form the beginnings of a cave. In time, a cave may become so large that the entire roof collapses to form a circular depression in the landscape called a swallow hole, a sinkhole, or a doline. The Minye doline in Papua New Guinea has vertical, clifflike walls and is 1,148 feet (350 m) wide and deep.

Such surface depressions and bare limestone pavements, fissured and etched (eaten into) by acid water, are typical of limestone karst landscapes. These landscapes are well developed in Slovenia and Guilin Province, China, where many caverns have collapsed.

The process of limestone solution goes both ways. Where there is evaporation of water rich in calcium bicarbonate, calcium carbonate is again precipitated (deposited). Dripping water forms stalactite deposits hanging from cave roofs and mound-shaped stalagmite (stuh-LAG-myt) deposits at splash points on cave floors.

A ⅕-inch (5-mm) wide stalactite has grown to 20 feet (6 m) in length in Easter Cave, Western Australia. Massive stalagmites have also grown in the Cottonwood and Carlsbad caves of New Mexico. Flowstone deposits may cover walls and floors of caves, creating terraces and dams filled with water and cave deposits such as the cave pearls of Jackson's Bay Cave in Jamaica.

Lava caves

Tunnels and caves can be formed in volcanic areas such as Hawaii and Iceland. The Kazumura Cave on the side of Kilauea volcano, for example, is a hollow lava tunnel that runs for 29 miles (47 km) downslope. It is 66 feet (20 m) below the surface and about 16 feet (5 m) in diameter. The tunnel was originally an open channel down which liquid lava flowed. Successive flows built up the sides of the channel and then roofed over it to form a tunnel.

Glacier caves and ice caves

Glacier caves form at the bottom of glaciers where ice in contact with rock melts to form meltwater streams. The streams enlarge their channels and may reach back up the valley for some distance below the glacier. The Paradise caves in the Mount Rainier glacier, for example, run for many miles. Glacier caves have relatively short lives because of the constant slow movement of glacier iceflows. Ice caves are more like normal rock caves in which the ice forms spectacular deposits, such as icicles like stalactite, and ice crystals from dripping water. Some ice formations in high mountain caves have become semi-permanent, such as those of Dachstein and Eisreisenwelt in the Austrian Alps.

An enormous cave has formed in the side of this iceberg.

Sea caves

Caves can be cut in almost any kind of rock by the power of the sea, which removes any weak rock. Sea caves are usually cut into the cliff bases where the wave action is most powerful. Fingal's Cave in the Scottish Hebrides is one example. The rocks here are upright jointed columns of lava. The wave action has pulled away some of these columns to form the cave.

Changes in the sea or land levels can leave sea caves high and dry. Changes can also submerge (push under the surface) sea caves, such as those found along the Mediterranean coast of France and Spain. Some of these caves are decorated with cave art and were clearly used by humans thousands of years ago when the caves could be reached above sea level. Spectacular submerged caves can also be found in the West Indies and in Florida.

Sandstone caves

Many of the cliff caves and rock shelters that were once occupied by the Pueblo Indians in western United States were originally cut by rivers. Winding rivers cut a number of notches into the bases of steep sandstone valley walls. Changes in river levels, especially down-cutting (the continual deepening of a river valley by flowing water), then left the notches suspended high and dry on cliff sides. Underground sandstone caves can also be formed in a way similar to limestone caves. Where the sand grains are held together by a natural cement of calcium carbonate, acid groundwater can remove the cement. The sand is then washed away to produce fissures, passages, and eventually caves. Sandstone caves with shafts (vertical openings) 985 feet (300 m) wide and up to 655 feet (200 m) deep can be found in some parts of Venezuela.

Cave dwellings cut into sandstone hundreds of years ago.

Cave dwellers

Many different types of creatures have found shelter and protection in caves over the ages. However, most life-forms shelter in caves for only some of the time. Cave-dwelling bats, for example, are night-flying creatures that use caves only for daytime shelter. Living in total darkness can result in blindness and loss of skin color, such as that found in the amphibian white salamander of the Slovenian caves.

Evidence in Bechan Cave, Utah, proves that even mammoths once used large caves. The floor of the cave is covered by a layer of trampled mammoth dung. Bears, lions, wolves, hyenas, and humans have all competed with one another for the use of caves in the past. Humans first used rock shelters and caves at least 230,000 years ago, as shown by the cave art, fire charcoal, and bones of animals they left behind. Some cave art dates back over 30,000 years.

Underwater sea caves provide shelter for some animals. For example, the coelacanth (SEE-luh-KANTH), a fish, lives in deep caves around the shores of Madagascar and some Indonesian islands during the day and hunts at night.

CHECK THESE OUT!
✔ACID AND BASE ✔CALCIUM ✔CARBON DIOXIDE ✔CLIFF ✔EROSION ✔FOSSIL ✔GEOLOGY ✔ICE AGE ✔RADIOCARBON DATING ✔VOLCANO

Cenozoic Era

The most recent phase of Earth's history

The Cenozoic (SEE-nuh-ZOH-ik) era covers the most recent 65 million years of Earth's history. Within this relatively short period of time there have been major changes to Earth. Great chains of mountains have been built, for example, and the global climate and the main forms of life have changed dramatically.

The Cenozoic era is divided into two periods: the Tertiary (TUHR-shee-ER-ee) from around 66 million to 1.6 million years ago, and the Quaternary (KWAH-tuhr-NER-ee) from around 1.6 million years ago to the present. The Tertiary is subdivided into five epochs (EH-puhks), from the oldest Paleocene (PAH-lee-uh-SEEN) through Eocene (EE-uh-SEEN), Oligocene (OH-lih-guh-SEEN), and Miocene (MY-uh-SEEN) to the Pliocene (PLY-uh-SEEN). The Quaternary has only two epochs, the Pleistocene (PLYS-tuh-SEEN) and the Holocene (HOH-luh-SEEN), which began a mere 10,000 years ago.

Cenozoic life and times

The Cenozoic is called the Age of Mammals because mammals replaced the dinosaurs as rulers of the land. The Cenozoic could also be thought of as the Age of Flowering Plants

The rocky landscape of Bryce Canyon, Utah, was formed during the Cenozoic era.

because the flowering plants, from palm trees to poppies and grasses, became more widespread, along with the insects that pollinated them.

The evolution of the grasses in Miocene times allowed the development of fast-running, plant-eating mammals. The spread of the grasses around the world was linked to climate cooling and smaller forests. This spread may also have encouraged human primate ancestors to leave the forests and, because the grasses often grew tall, may have speeded up their ability to walk upright on two legs and to work together for safety. Five million years ago, in late Tertiary times, the hominids (HAH-muh-NIDZ; the ancestors of humans and some apes) evolved in Africa, from where they eventually spread around the world.

In the Americas, uplift (formation) of the Sierra Nevada, Cascade, and Rocky Mountains led to a cooler and drier climate with extensive grasslands occupied by grazing mammals such as the early horses. In northwest America, rising

HIGHLIGHTS

◆ The Cenozoic era is the most recent phase of geological history, from 65 million years ago to the present day.

◆ The Cenozoic era is divided into the Tertiary and Quaternary periods.

◆ Climate changes during the Cenozoic era had important impacts on the evolution of plants and mammals, including humans.

◆ Today's continents are largely the result of geological and climatic changes that took place during the Cenozoic era.

hot rocks from within Earth forced their way to the surface and erupted to form the vast lava (LAH-vuh) pile of the Snake River Plateau. The hotsprings and geysers of Yellowstone National Park are the most recent signs of continuing volcanic activity in the region. As sea levels fell, North and South America were eventually joined by a land bridge. Organisms could move back and forth between the continents.

During Tertiary times the continent of India finally moved to join with Asia. The rocks in between were crumpled to form the Himalaya Mountains. As the mountain chain was pushed up, it formed a great barrier between Asia and India. This barrier changed the climate of the region, forming the Southeast Asian monsoon. Also in Tertiary times, Africa moved northward, and plate collisions in southern Europe folded the Alps and separated the Mediterranean Sea from the Atlantic. The Mediterranean gradually dried out, forming vast salt deposits before being flooded again about five million years ago.

The Ice Age

Around four million years ago global climates began to cool so much that the polar ice caps formed and began to grow. By Quaternary times the world was in the grip of an ice age, with alternating cold and warmer phases. At the height of the ice age so much water was locked up in the ice caps and glaciers (large bodies of ice) that the sea level fell by around 330 feet (100 m), exposing the continental shelves that lie between the shoreline and the continental slope. Land bridges were formed, such as the Bering Strait. Animals and modern humans traveled across the Strait from Asia into North America.

At its maximum, the North American ice sheet covered 5 million square miles (13 million sq km). The ice reached as far south as the Great Lakes, which

The woolly mammoth was well protected against the cold.

formed when the ice sheet finally melted. The ice cap over Scandinavia was about 2½ miles (4 km) thick and so heavy that it weighed down the surface of the land. The flow of glaciers in mountainous regions cut through even the hardest rocks, deepening valleys into distinctive U-shaped cross sections. The rock debris (duh-BREE; broken pieces) was carried to lower ground and deposited. Ice flow over these layers of debris molded it into a variety of forms, such as egg-shaped drumlins (low hills).

In the northern hemisphere, animals of the ice age, such as the woolly mammoth and woolly rhinoceros, and the tough Neanderthal people of Europe were adapted to the cold. However, they all died when the climate finally improved and the ice sheets and glaciers melted around 15,000 years ago. Enormous volumes of water and rock debris were released over the landscapes. Meltwater was dammed into huge lakes, such as the Great Lakes, by glacial debris. Meltwater lakes such as Lake Missoula, near today's Seattle, sometimes flooded the surrounding landscape with huge power and terrible effects, to produce the Channeled Scablands of Washington State.

As the ice continued to melt, sea levels worldwide rose and flooded the continental shelves. In far northern regions, such as Arctic Canada, Scandinavia, and Scotland, the land is still slowly rising since the end of the ice age when the weight of ice was removed.

CHECK THESE OUT!
✔CLIMATE ✔CONTINENT
✔GEOLOGIC TIMESCALE
✔ICE AGE ✔QUATERNARY
PERIOD ✔TERTIARY
PERIOD

Centripetal and Centrifugal Forces

Forces experienced by an object moving in a curved or circular path

Newton's first law of motion states that objects remain at rest or move in a straight line at constant speed unless acted on by a force. If an object is to move in a circular or curved motion it must experience a force directed toward the center of that circle. This inward force is called the centripetal (sen-TRIH-puh-tuhl) force. However, the object moving around the curve seems to experience a force directed outward from this center. This outward force is called centrifugal (sen-TRIH-fyuh-guhl) force.

HIGHLIGHTS

- A centripetal force is needed to make an object move in a circular or curved path.

- Centrifugal force is the apparent force that observers traveling in a curved path feel acting on themselves and on other objects.

- For every action there is an equal and opposite reaction. This law explains the opposite effects of centripetal and centrifugal forces.

- Centrifugal force can be used to separate components of different masses from a mixture.

Experiencing centrifugal force

Imagine someone holding a string at one end with a rock tied on the other, swinging it around their head in a circle. It would feel as though the rock was trying to pull the string out of the person's hands as it swings. It would be as if there were a centrifugal force pulling or pushing the rock away from the center of the circle.

The clearest clue that centrifugal force is not what it seems comes if the person suddenly lets go of the string. The rock does not keep going around in a circle because centripetal force is needed for that. Instead the rock flies off in a straight line, in the direction of its velocity (vuh-LAH-suh-tee; its speed and direction) at the moment the string is released. The force of gravity would then bring the rock to the ground.

As the rock moves in the circle, its speed remains the same, but its velocity constantly changes because its direction is constantly changing. The rock is being pulled inward with the string to keep it moving in a circle. The only force acting on the rock is this centripetal force toward the center.

This centrifuge is used at the astronaut training center in Cologne, Germany.

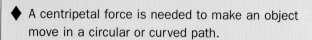

Forces in a Cornering Car

A common example of centrifugal force is the force experienced by a driver in a car going around a corner. The driver feels pushed toward the outside of the curve toward the driver's door. This outward centrifugal force is the result of the car moving in a circular path. In the diagram, centripetal force (F_p) is the inward force that must be exerted to keep an object (the car) moving in a circle. The centripetal force in this example is supplied by the friction between the car's tires and the road. The driver, whose body has a natural tendency to keep going in a straight line, feels the effects of this inward centripetal force as an outward centrifugal force. The car seat and seat belt push on the driver with a force F_p. The driver's body presses against them with an equal and opposite reaction force.

The car as a whole experiences a centrifugal force pushing it toward the outside edge of the curve. In this case, the car's natural tendency to fly off the road is balanced by a centripetal force (F_p) resulting from the friction between the tires and the road surface. In both cases, the centrifugal force is a result of the driver or the car's inertia, which is the tendency to keep moving with the same velocity unless acted on by a force. If the car is going too fast, its inertia might overcome the friction between the tires and the road, and the car will begin to skid off the road. Skidding was a problem on the Indianapolis 500 racetrack until the track was redesigned, forcing the drivers to slow down when cornering.

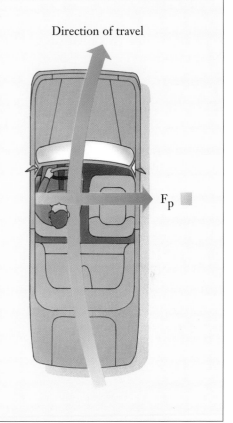

Direction of travel

F_p

The reason the force seems to go in the other direction is the principle of action and reaction. English physicist Sir Isaac Newton (1642–1727) discovered this principle, making it one of his three basic laws of mechanics (the movements of particles). He said that for every action there is an equal and opposite reaction. In other words, because someone pulls on the rock, the rock also pulls on the person.

Using centrifugal force

Centrifugal force has useful properties. The strength of the force acting on an object depends on its inertia (ih-NUHR-shuh; the tendency to keep moving with the same velocity unless acted on by a force), which is another measure of its mass. An object weighing 4½ pounds (2 kg), for example, experiences twice as much centrifugal force as one weighing 2¼ pounds (1 kg) spinning at the same rate. The force also gets much larger the faster an object is turning. Doubling the speed quadruples the centrifugal force.

A centrifuge (SEN-truh-fyooj) is a machine that uses this principle to separate out particles with different densities in a mixture. Medical centrifuges separate blood cells from the liquid plasma in which they are normally suspended. Blood is placed in a test tube that is fastened to the middle of the centrifuge and then spun at high speed. Blood cells have a higher density than the fluid around them, so the centrifugal force acting on them is largest. This force pushes the cells to the outside edge of the test tube. Usually the test tube swings into a horizontal position in the centrifuge so the cells gather at the bottom and the clear blood plasma remains near the top.

Astronauts train in giant centrifuges to get used to the gravitational forces experienced in flight. Roller-coaster rides also use the centrifuge principle. Centrifugal force is what keeps people from falling out as they loop-the-loop.

CHECK THESE OUT!
✔FORCE ✔GRAVITY ✔NEWTONIAN PHYSICS

Chemical Reaction

Any process that leads to the formation of new chemical substances

Processes as different as TNT exploding and a plant growing all occur through chemical reactions. Chemical reactions also provide the heat of a gas stove, change the flavor of food as it cooks, and happen as someone breathes.

A changing world

Substances may be changed in three ways: by physical changes, nuclear changes, and chemical changes. Physical changes include melting and boiling. Nuclear changes involve the nuclei (NOO-klee-eye; centers) of atoms.

Chemical changes alter the way the atoms in substances group together. In the simplest cases, a single substance splits into two or more

HIGHLIGHTS

◆ Chemical reactions cause changes in the atomic combinations of mixtures.

◆ The number of atoms of each element in a mixture is not changed by a chemical reaction.

◆ Some reactions are reversible, so the reaction can go forward or backward, depending on conditions.

◆ Chemical reactions can be made to go faster by adding a catalyst or by increasing the temperature.

substances when it is heated. An example of this type of reaction happens as part of the oil-refining process. Thick, heavy oils are cracked (split) by heat. The large molecules (MAH-lih-KYOOLZ; atoms bonded together) at the start of the reaction are heated until they vibrate so much that they shake themselves apart. At the end of the reaction the atoms that were present in the starting material are grouped in smaller molecules. In other chemical reactions, two or more different substances exchange some atoms and form different substances in the process.

Balancing the books

A key point in chemical reactions is that the numbers of atoms of each element (substance with one kind of atom) are the same before and after the reaction. In addition, the overall electrical charge and mass of material must stay the same because the number of atoms also stays the same. Together these rules help chemists to work out exactly the reaction if they know the starting material and one of the products.

An explosive chemical reaction helps to demolish a building in a city center.

The formulas showing the composition of chemical substances are represented using a system first drawn up by Swedish chemist Jöns Jakob Berzelius (1779–1848). Each element has a symbol of one or two letters. In most cases, the symbol is a shortened version of the English name. Sometimes the symbol comes from another language. The symbol for iron, Fe, comes from the Latin word *ferrum*. If there is more than one atom of an element, the number is shown as a small numeral to the right and below the symbol. For example, the formula of water is H_2O, since each molecule of water contains two hydrogen atoms (H) and one oxygen atom (O).

Because of the way the atoms are arranged, for metals or ionic compounds the formulas are usually written as ratios of elements. Thus a chemist writes NaCl for table salt to indicate that it is made of sodium chloride and that there are equal amounts of sodium and chlorine.

A firework display is a colorful and noisy chemical reaction enjoyed by many.

A combination of symbols such as NaCl is called a formula unit. When the substance is composed of molecules (MAH-lih-KYOOLZ), each made up of a particular combination of atoms, the molecular formula is used, for example, C_2H_6 for the compound ethane.

Chemical reactions are written as an equation. The chemicals present before the reaction (the reactants) are written on the left of an arrow that points to the chemicals present after the reaction (the reaction products). As an example, sodium hydroxide (NaOH) reacts with sulfuric acid (H_2SO_4) to make sodium sulfate (Na_2SO_4) and water (H_2O). The equation is written as follows:

$$2NaOH + H_2SO_4 \rightarrow Na_2SO_4 + 2H_2O$$

The number 2 before the formula for sodium hydroxide shows that two formula units of sodium hydroxide react with one molecule of sulfuric acid to make one formula unit of sodium sulfate and two molecules of water. Counting each kind of atom on either side of the arrow shows that there are two sodium atoms on the left then two on the right, six oxygen atoms on the left then six on the right, four hydrogen atoms on the left then four on the right, and one sulfur atom on the left then one on the right. The equation balances.

LOOK CLOSER

Reaction Speed

Different mixtures of the same materials react at different speeds. The speed of a chemical reaction depends on a number of factors, such as concentration, surface area, temperature, and the presence of catalysts. If concentrated solutions of chemicals are mixed together, they will react more quickly than dilute mixtures. This is because the atoms and molecules need to collide for a reaction to occur between them. If the solution is more concentrated, collisions between molecules that can react will be more frequent and the reaction will then be more likely to take place.

Solids can react only at their surfaces. If a solid is finely ground, it has a larger surface area than the same weight of identical coarsely ground solid. This is why sawdust burns much faster than a log. If the temperature of a mixture increases, the atoms and molecules in that mixture start to move faster. They bump into each other harder and more often, which makes the reaction faster. A catalyst is a substance that makes a reaction go faster by helping atoms and molecules to react with each other.

Reversible Reactions: A Molecular Party

When hydrogen and iodine are heated together so that the iodine vaporizes (VAY-puh-ryz-uhz; turns into a gas), they react to produce some hydrogen iodide. However, the violet color of the iodine vapor never completely disappears because not all of the iodine reacts. This is because as soon as the hydrogen iodide is formed, some of it starts to turn back to hydrogen and iodine. The reaction is written as follows: $H_2 + I_2 \leftrightarrow 2HI$.

Both reactions occur at the same time, producing a mixture of H_2, I_2, and HI. When the backward and forward reactions both happen at the same speed, the reactions are said to be in equilibrium (ee-kwuh-LIH-bree-uhm; balance). If a small amount of iodine is mixed with a much larger amount of hydrogen, however, the mixture becomes almost completely colorless, showing that almost all the iodine has been used up by the reaction.

It is easy to understand why this happens by thinking about the molecules that are reacting. To have a chance of reacting together, two molecules first find each other. At the start of the reaction, each iodine (I_2) molecule is constantly being jostled by hydrogen (H_2) molecules. Every so often, a collision will result in a reaction between an H_2 molecule and an I_2 molecule, producing two molecules of hydrogen iodide (HI). The HI molecules then drift off into the mixture.

For the reverse reaction to occur, the reaction that produces H_2 and I_2, two HI molecules have to bump into each other. However, if there is a lot of hydrogen in the mixture, each HI molecule will spend a great deal of time bumping into H_2 molecules before it finds its perfect partner (HI) for the reverse reaction. An H_2 molecule and an HI molecule can react together, but without making a difference to the mixture. In the meantime, the I_2 molecules are being changed into hydrogen iodide by the H_2 molecules.

If more iodine is added, the surplus hydrogen molecules will change that iodine into more hydrogen iodide. After a point, though, there is so much hydrogen iodide in the mixture that it is no longer difficult for two HI molecules to meet. That is when the reverse reaction starts to compete, and the forward and backward reactions gradually match each other.

Numbers and weights

Once the equation for a reaction is known, the weights of the reactants and the products can be calculated from their atomic weights. For the reaction between sodium hydroxide and sulfuric acid, for example, the atomic weights are H: 1; Na: 23; O: 16; S: 32. The formula weights of the materials in the reaction can be worked out by adding together the atomic weights:

Formula weight (NaOH) = 23 + 16 + 1 = 40
Formula weight (H_2SO_4) = (1 x 2) + 32 + (16 x 4)
$\qquad$ = 98

So 40 grams of sodium hydroxide react with 98 grams of sulfuric acid, for example.

Reversible reactions

The arrow in a chemical equation shows which chemicals are considered the reactants of the reaction and which are considered the products. In reality, many reactions can go forward or backward. These reactions are called reversible reactions. A double-headed arrow is used in the equation to show that the reaction can occur in both directions. A good example of a reversible reaction happens between hydrogen (H_2) and iodine (I_2). The reaction is written as follows: $H_2 + I_2 \leftrightarrow 2HI$.

Driving forces

Some reactions happen spontaneously (by themselves) when substances are mixed. The reaction between sodium and chlorine is a good example. If sodium metal comes into contact with chlorine gas, a violent reaction occurs that has the following equation: $2Na + Cl_2 \rightarrow 2NaCl$.

When the reaction occurs, sodium atoms lose electrons (negatively charged particles) and become positively charged sodium ions (Na^+). The chlorine molecules take up these electrons

Iron ore, coke, and limestone are put in a blast furnace. Steel, gases, and insoluble slag are produced.

and form negatively charged chloride ions (Cl⁻). Because of their opposite charges, these two types of ions are strongly attracted to each other. They form a very stable (unreactive) salt called sodium chloride (NaCl). In this case, the driving force of the reaction is the stability of the salt.

Few reactions are driven forward as strongly as the sodium–chlorine reaction. In fact many chemists spend most of their time trying to force reactions to go the right way to produce the products they want. One of the most effective ways of doing this is to remove a reaction product so it cannot react with other reaction products and thereby return to the starting materials. There are a number of ways of doing this, depending on whether the product to be removed is a solid, a liquid, or a gas.

A solid reaction product can be removed by freezing it out of a mixture or if it is insoluble (in-SAHL-yuh-buhl; cannot be dissolved in liquid) in that mixture. Either way the solid product can no longer take part in the reaction. When a solution of lead nitrate ($Pb(NO_3)_2$) mixes with a solution of potassium iodide (KI), for example, the following reaction occurs:

$$Pb(NO_3)_2 + 2KI \rightarrow PbI_2 + 2KNO_3$$

As soon as the solutions come into contact, clouds of solid lead iodide (PbI_2) form. Because lead iodide is insoluble in water, most of the lead iodide is locked away in crystals. The potassium nitrate (KNO_3) stays in solution.

When a reaction in a mixture of liquids produces a gas, that gas is allowed to escape from the reaction mixture. It can no longer react with the other products and so the reverse reaction is prevented. An example is the reaction between sodium carbonate ($NaCO_3$) and hydrochloric acid (HCl):

$$NaCO_3 + HCl \rightarrow NaCl + CO_2 + H_2O.$$

Carbon dioxide (CO_2) bubbles out of the mixture and cannot react further.

In the reaction between acetic acid (CH_3COOH) and butanol (C_4H_9OH), the reaction is made to go forward by boiling away the water while the butyl

acetate ($CH_3COOC_4H_9$) is formed:
$$CH_3COOH + C_4H_9OH \rightarrow CH_3COOC_4H_9 + H_2O$$

Heat and catalysis

When molecules that could react collide, they often bounce off each other without reacting. This is because they do not have enough energy to break the existing bonds between their atoms and then remake them with other atoms to form the reaction products.

There are two ways of improving the chances of a reaction happening. The simple way is to increase the temperature of the mixture. This makes the molecules move faster and collide with more energy. The only problem with this approach is that higher temperatures can set off reactions other than the one that is wanted.

The second way is to use a catalyst (KA-tuhl-uhst). A catalyst is a chemical that enables a chemical reaction to happen at a faster rate or at a lower temperature. The catalyst reacts easily with the starting materials to form an intermediate (middle) product. The intermediate product then breaks up to form

College students learn about the right reactants and conditions for a range of chemical reactions.

the final products and return the catalyst to its original state. In effect, one slow reaction is replaced by two quick ones.

Start all over again

Chemists use the term *yield* to describe the amount of the starting mixture of a reaction that changes into the product they want to make. Industrial chemists often use low-yield reactions but manage to turn all their raw materials into product. How do they do this? The answer is simple—recycling.

In chemical plants, reactions are performed in tanks called reactors. The starting materials are fed in at one end and the product mixture is collected at the other. The desired product is then separated out of the mixture.

Separation is often carried out by a process called distillation (DIS-tuh-LAY-shuhn) in which a liquid is boiled off and the steam is condensed to reform the liquid. The rest of the mixture is then pumped back to the start of the reactor and topped up with more reactants. The mixture passes through the reactor again and more of it turns into product.

CHECK THESE OUT!
✔ATOM ✔CATALYST ✔CHEMISTRY ✔COMPOUND
✔ELEMENT ✔EVAPORATION AND BOILING
✔MIXTURE ✔MOLECULE ✔OIL ✔PHYSICAL CHANGE

Chemistry

The study of the structure of matter and the transformations it undergoes

At some point in history—certainly by the time of the ancient Chinese, Egyptians, and Greeks—people became curious about the nature and behavior of objects around them. They wanted to know why rocks, water, and wood appeared and behaved in different ways, for example. Various beliefs and theories developed, many based more on philosophy than on experiment, before this ancient curiosity led to the modern sciences of chemistry and physics.

The roots of practical chemistry are also ancient. As long ago as 4000 B.C.E. the Egyptians used chemical reactions to extract copper from malachite (MA-luh-KYT), a green, striped mineral. It is likely that the Egyptians learned their methods by accident or by trial and error. Modern chemists rely less on trial and error and more on using scientific theories and methods in their experiments.

HIGHLIGHTS

◆ The earliest form of practical chemistry was called alchemy. It was first practiced in Egypt and China in around the 1st century C.E.

◆ In the early 19th century, Swedish chemist Jöns Jakob Berzelius developed the system that is still used to write chemical equations.

◆ Hydrogen, the simplest and lightest element, was discovered by Henry Cavendish in 1766.

◆ Biochemistry is a branch of chemistry that studies living organisms in detail. It helps us to understand illnesses and contributes useful information toward drug design.

The Greek philosophers

Between the 7th and 4th centuries B.C.E., a number of Greek philosophers produced theories about the nature of substances. The first of them was Thales (around 625–547 B.C.E.). Thales observed that all creatures required water to survive. He suggested that all substances were made from water.

Anaximander (610–around 547 B.C.E.), a student of Thales, changed Thales's theory by proposing a universal substance called *apeiron* (meaning unlimited). Anaximander believed that *apeiron* contained all possible opposites, such as heat and cold, dryness and wetness, and hardness and softness. In his thinking, all substances on Earth were made by taking apart *apeiron* and mixing its selected parts.

Later, Anaximenes (570–500 B.C.E.) proposed a different theory. He said that air was a compressed form of fire and could be compressed to form water, which could be compressed to

Seventeenth-century alchemists were thought to be capable of creative wonders. This cartoon shows an alchemist creating human life from a topaz crystal.

STORY OF SCIENCE

Robert Boyle—A Skeptical Chemist

Robert Boyle was born in Ireland in 1627 into a scientific family—both his sisters wrote a science book. He was one of the first people to approach the study of substances in a rigorously scientific way. He used careful experimental methods that anyone could repeat to confirm his results. He disputed the theory that all substances consisted of mixtures of the four elements. He pointed out that smoke, thought to be a form of air at the time, was a mixture of soot, moisture, and oils, among other things. Smoke could not, therefore, be a form of the so-called element air.

While he was studying air, Boyle noted that a sample of the gas reduced in volume when put under pressure. He concluded from this observation that gases consist of tiny particles, surrounded by space, that could be pushed closer together under pressure. This theory was similar to that of Democritus in the 5th century B.C.E. Scientists now know this to be true. Boyle also noted that a sample of metal becomes heavier when it rusts or reacts with air in some other way. He decided that the increase in weight was caused by particles in air combining with particles in the metal sample and forming a solid. In 1661, he combined the results of his experiments and put forward his theory of atoms in a book entitled *The Skeptical Chemist*.

form earth. The philosopher Empedocles (around 490–430 B.C.E.) then combined the earlier theories by proposing that all substances on Earth were made of the four elements: air, earth, fire, and water. Different combinations of the four elements, he believed, produced substances with different properties.

Democritus (around 460–370 B.C.E.) believed these four elements were in the form of tiny particles, which he called atoms. His theory did not become popular at the time. Finally, Aristotle (384–322 B.C.E.) adopted Empedocles's theory and added a fifth element called aither or ether, which made up the heavens.

The alchemists

The earliest form of practical chemistry was called alchemy (AL-kuh-mee), and its Western principles were laid down by Mary the Jewess, who lived in Alexandria in the 1st century C.E. So many of the early alchemists were women that this early science was called *opus mulierum*, the work of women. Alchemy started to be practiced in Egypt and China around the 1st century C.E.

Alchemists tried to find a method for turning base metals, such as lead, into gold. The Chinese alchemists believed gold to be the perfect medicine and the route to eternal life. Alchemists in Egypt were simply trying to make gold. Arab alchemists combined the Chinese and Egyptian versions of alchemy. They produced chemical recipes with quantities of the materials to be used. This mixed form of alchemy spread to Europe in the 11th century.

Although they failed in their attempts to make gold from lead, the alchemists devised several useful chemical reagents and techniques as they mixed and separated substances over the centuries. In particular, the technique of distillation (DIS-tuh-LAY-shuhn) made it possible to produce pure samples of alcohol, ammonia, and various acids.

Chemistry becomes a science

By the 16th century, alchemists were using their methods to measure the purity of metal ores and to produce medicines. For both tasks it was important to know the weights of the ingredients used and the products formed. As alchemists

Antoine Lavoisier discovered that air consists of oxygen and nitrogen.

started to perform experiments more precisely, some of them became suspicious of the four-element theory. Among the doubters was Robert Boyle (1627–1691). In the 17th century, Boyle's careful experiments suggested that Democritus's theory of atoms might be correct and that particles in air combine with metals to form oxides such as rust. Although Boyle was on the right track (see the box on page 124), some chemists were distracted by the phlogiston (floh-JIS-tuhn) theory until the late 18th century.

The first true elements

In 1766, British chemist and physicist Henry Cavendish (1731–1810) discovered a gas that was produced by reacting metals with acids. Finding that the gas burned, Cavendish called this gas inflammable air, not knowing he had discovered hydrogen, the simplest and lightest element.

In the 1770s, further important discoveries were made. In separate experiments, British chemist Joseph Priestley (1733–1804) and Swedish chemist Carl Scheele (1742–1772) both discovered the oxygen in air. Priestley called this

gas dephlogisticated (dee-floh-JIS-tih-kay-tuhd) air, while Scheele called it fire air. Both names were given because of oxygen's ability to support combustion (burning). Scheele also discovered a second gas in air, which he named foul air, and which did not support burning.

French chemists Antoine (1743–1794) and Marie (1758–1836) Lavoisier studied how materials react with air. They compared their results with those of Priestley and Scheele. They found that the part of air that reacted with sulfur and phosphorus was the same as that involved in combustion. They named this gas oxygen.

DISCOVERERS

James Sumner

Biochemistry (the chemistry of living organisms) began to grow as a distinct branch of science in the 20th century. One of its pioneers was U.S. biochemist James Sumner (1887–1955). Since 1857, when French chemist Louis Pasteur (1822–1895) discovered fermentation, scientists have known that certain living organisms make specific chemical reactions happen. In the case of fermentation, yeast changes sugar into alcohol and carbon dioxide. At first, it was thought that cells in the yeast itself were somehow causing fermentation to happen. In 1897, German chemist Eduard Buchner (1860–1917) found that a solution of the chemicals in yeast cells caused fermentation even if the cells themselves were removed. These chemicals were called enzymes.

Scientists studied the action of enzymes for many years without being able to purify them and identify their chemical composition. James Sumner believed that it should be possible to obtain pure crystals of enzymes. He also believed that enzymes were proteins. This belief was disputed by many experts at the time. Their opinions changed in 1926, when James Sumner produced crystals of the enzyme urease (YOOR-ee-ayz) from jack beans. With his colleague John Northrop (1891–1987), Sumner was able to confirm that the crystals were made of the same material that causes urea to decompose in plants. They then used chemical tests to successfully prove Sumner's theory that enzymes were proteins.

Chemistry is widely taught in schools. This student carries out an experiment supervised by her teacher.

The Lavoisiers gave the name *azote*, from the Greek word meaning "without life," to the part of air that did not support burning in Scheele's experiments. Azote was later renamed nitrogen. By the time of his death, Antoine Lavoisier had produced a table of 33 elements. He defined an element as a substance that could not be broken down by chemical methods. Of the 33 original elements, 26 were true elements. Five were later found to be compounds, since they could be broken down by chemical means, and two, light and heat, were energy rather than matter.

Chemical equations

Lavoisier's table of elements stimulated scientists to find out more about the elements and their chemical reactions. In 1803, British scientist John Dalton (1766–1844) proposed that atoms of the elements reacted together to form molecules. Dalton's first theory was not quite correct,

LOOK CLOSER

The Rise and Fall of Phlogiston

Ever since Greek philosopher Empedocles (around 490–430 B.C.E.) put forward the idea that fire was an element, scholars and philosophers have wanted to understand more about fire. In particular, they wanted to know why some substances burned and others did not. It took more than 2,000 years for a reasonable, but incorrect, theory to arrive. In the late 17th century, German chemist Johann Becher (1635–1682) and his student Georg Stahl (1660–1734) observed that materials became lighter when they burned. They believed that this loss of weight was caused by a substance leaving the material. Stahl went on to call this material phlogiston. In Stahl's theory, only materials that contained phlogiston could burn. On burning, materials such as coal or wood lost their phlogiston to the air and turned into ash.

In the 18th century, Stahl developed the phlogiston theory to cover reactions apart from combustion (burning). In his belief, metals that rusted were also losing phlogiston to the air. Many chemists of the time used the phlogiston theory to explain the results of their own work. For example, when Joseph Priestley discovered oxygen in 1774, he named it dephlogisticated air. Priestley observed that oxygen made substances burn more strongly than they do in air. He believed this to be because normal air already contained some phlogiston.

However, the phlogiston theory was to be disproved soon after Priestley made his discovery. In 1772, Antoine and Marie Lavoisier started their own studies of burning sulfur and phosphorus. By carefully collecting and weighing the products of combustion, they discovered that substances actually gained weight when they burned. They found the same to be true of rusting metals. They worked out that burning and rusting materials were not losing phlogiston to the air but gaining something from the air. Since sulfur and phosphorus both produce acids when they burn, they named this component of air oxygen, meaning "acid former." They went on to study the reactions of oxygen and its role in animal and plant respiration (energy production). By the end of the 18th century, their ideas had replaced the phlogiston theory.

however, since he had thought that one atom of each element reacted. It was later found that atoms of the elements react in simple ratios. Dalton then used the corrected ratios to produce a table of atomic weights for other elements.

Around the time of Dalton's work, Swedish chemist Jöns Jakob Berzelius (1779–1848) developed a system of symbols that is still used to represent chemical equations. For example, the reaction between hydrogen and oxygen can be written as follows:

$$2H_2 + O_2 \rightarrow 2H_2O$$

This equation shows that two hydrogen (H_2) molecules react with one oxygen (O_2) molecule to form one water (H_2O) molecule; hydrogen and oxygen molecules each consist of two atoms, and water molecules consist of two hydrogen and one oxygen atom.

The periodic table

By the 1860s, 63 elements had been discovered. Chemists had studied the reactions of these elements and collected a lot of information about the behaviors of the individual elements. Russian chemist Dmitri Mendeleyev (1834–1907) noticed that certain properties of the elements vary in a repeating pattern as the atomic weight increases. In 1869, Mendeleyev constructed a table of elements in which he placed elements with similar properties above each other in rows. This original classification of chemical elements was arranged according to relative atomic mass. There were some gaps in the table at first, but Mendeleyev correctly predicted that the gaps would be filled by undiscovered elements. He was even able to predict the properties of some missing elements. His predictions were confirmed when the elements were discovered.

A computer chip, made possible by inorganic chemistry.

Specialization

As the amount of chemical knowledge grew spectacularly through the late 19th and 20th centuries, chemists started to concentrate on particular aspects of chemistry. Most of the chemistry that took place before the 19th century concentrated on minerals and ores. This type of chemistry would now be called inorganic chemistry. The modern inorganic chemical industry produces a variety of materials, from cement to glass and from synthetic gems to steel. New inorganic materials include superconductors that conduct electricity with almost no resistance.

During the 19th century, scientists learned more about organic compounds, which are chemical compounds that occur in living organisms. They found that all organic compounds contained carbon and most contained hydrogen. The term *organic chemistry* now refers to the study of carbon compounds in general, including those that are produced from coal and oil. The organic chemical industry produces a wide range of materials, including dyes, explosives, fibers, fuel, and plastics.

Twentieth-century improvements in laboratory techniques made it possible to study the chemistry of living organisms in detail. This field of chemistry is now called biochemistry. Biochemistry helps to understand illnesses and provides information for drug research. A further branch of chemistry, called physical chemistry, specializes in the structure of atoms and molecules, as well as the factors that determine whether and how rapidly a reaction will occur.

CHECK THESE OUT!
✔ACID AND BASE ✔ATOM ✔CHEMICAL REACTION ✔ORGANIC CHEMISTRY ✔PERIODIC TABLE ✔PHYSICAL CHEMISTRY ✔THERMODYNAMICS

Clay

A fine-grained material that is easily molded when mixed with water

Clay is a fine-grained material that has many uses, mainly because it is soft and easily molded when it is wet. This quality is called plasticity. Clay then keeps its molded shape when it dries naturally or is fired. It is used to make bricks, pottery, porcelain, tiles, cement, and many other products. Bricks are made by drying or baking clay that has been shaped in molds.

Clay is easy to mold because it is made of tiny particles or grains, that are too small for the eye to see. In all true clays, more than half the particles have a diameter smaller than 0.0041 mm. The main ingredients of clay minerals are small crystals of

Clay is a good material for pottery because it is easy to mold and then holds the shape after firing.

silica (silicon dioxide, SiO_2), combined with one or several metals such as aluminum (symbol Al), magnesium (Mg), iron (Fe), potassium (K), sodium (Na), or calcium (Ca).

Clay is common in rocks such as shales and mudstones. It is found in deserts, sandy beaches, sandstones, deep-sea silts, and mud in many parts of the world. Clay may be gray, black, white, or yellowish in color. It usually becomes powdery when dry. Often clay is found in the form of a clay gall, small chips of clay that have hardened and dried elsewhere before being carried to their present site. When clay is heated or subjected to great pressure, the water is squeezed out of it, and the material forms hard rocks called mudstone or shale.

How clay is made

Like all sedimentary rocks, clay is the result of many natural processes. The first step in the formation of clay comes when other rocks are broken up into small fragments through the

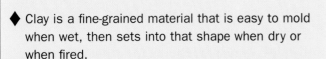

HIGHLIGHTS

◆ Clay is a fine-grained material that is easy to mold when wet, then sets into that shape when dry or when fired.

◆ Clay is common in sedimentary rocks such as shales and mudstones.

◆ Clay minerals are crystals of silica combined with metal elements, most often aluminum, but sometimes magnesium or iron instead or as well.

◆ Clay minerals are most commonly formed when silicates are changed by hydrothermal fluids rising through the rocks from below.

◆ The most common clay structure is called sheet-silicate, a crystal structure that, like paper, is much larger in two dimensions than in three.

processes of weathering and erosion (wearing away). Rain, ice, wind, and small living organisms including bacteria and lichen (LY-kuhn) help to break down the rock. Rain dissolves the surface of the rock. The bacteria and lichen break up the rock, as does ice. Wind moves away the small pieces that have broken off.

The small fragments of rock are then carried by rivers to a new site, often on a seabed or a riverbed. There, the fragments are covered with water and buried under soil or other rocks. Chemical changes take place to produce clay. The type of clay that results depends on the nature of the rock fragments and the circumstances in which the clay is formed. Clays can also be produced solely in the sea or deep underground, when minerals are subjected to hydrothermal fluids. These fluids are chemically rich, active, hot waters rising through Earth's crust from deep underneath it.

Structure of clay

The most common clay structure is called sheet silicate. Just as paper is much larger and longer than it is thick, clay minerals have a crystal structure that is much larger in two dimensions than in three. This sheetlike crystal structure is called a layer lattice. The lattice means that all clay minerals have a high surface area in relation to their mass and thickness.

This sheetlike structure also means that clay absorbs large amounts of water. When it is ground up, sieved, and then mixed with water, clay increases its volume by absorbing water onto the surfaces of its crystals. The resulting paste is what most people think of as clay: a material that is soft and can be shaped and molded, and then hardens when it is dried or fired.

CHECK THESE OUT!
✔MINERALOGY ✔ROCK ✔SEDIMENTARY ROCK

LOOK CLOSER

Types of Clay

Different types of clay contain different minerals. These metals blend into the clay's layer lattice in various ways, producing different crystal structures. Kaolinite is the most common clay. It is formed when feldspar is rotted by hydrothermal fluids underground. Kaolinite contains aluminum. Sometimes it occurs in massive white layers in sedimentary rocks. Kaolinite is used to make china, pottery, and porcelain. It is mined in Devon and Cornwall in England, and in Colorado, Pennsylvania, Virginia, Georgia, and South Carolina in the United States.

Montmorillonite is another common clay. It results when the original minerals are buried or subjected to hydrothermal fluids. Montmorillonite contains aluminum and sometimes also magnesium and iron. Fuller's earth, a type of montmorillonite, is a volcanic clay. This very fine-grained clay is used as a bleaching agent and to refine oils and fats. It was originally used for degreasing woolen fabrics.

Illite is the third common clay. It contains potassium and aluminum and sometimes iron and magnesium as well. Other clays may contain magnesium, aluminum, and iron and are sometimes formed in very cold climates, for example, in Antarctica. Some clays containing aluminium and magnesium have needle-shaped lattice structures, which form long ribbons or chains of crystals.

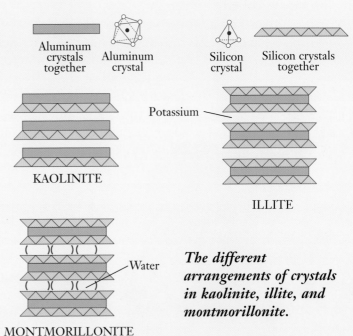

The different arrangements of crystals in kaolinite, illite, and montmorillonite.

Cliff

Steep wall of rock or earth

Some of Earth's most dramatic land features are cliffs. Often they are at their most impressive along the coast. Cliffs are steep walls of rock or earth that occur where the surface of the land falls away abruptly. They vary in height, ranging from low walls only tens of feet high to steep precipices (PRES-uh-pis-ez; headlands) hundreds of feet tall.

Cliff formation is linked to two natural processes. These processes are geologic uplift (the land rises or the sea level falls) and erosion, where the rocks on Earth's surface are worn away by natural forces such as wind and water.

How sea cliffs form

The form and appearance of sea cliffs depend on the physical features of the land, the type and structure of the rocks from which they are made, and the kinds of erosion they experience, which are closely related to climate and latitude.

The type of rock from which the cliffs are made determines the speed at which they are eroded (worn away). As sea cliffs are being eroded, so the edge of the coast moves further inland, and the sea encroaches (advances). This process is called cliff retreat.

Northwestern Europe has many dramatic sea cliffs. Here, the land has risen up relatively quickly since the end of the last ice age. As the great ice caps and glaciers that covered and pressed down

Cliffs are typical coastline features.

the land melted, a great weight of ice was removed and the land began to rise again. Over the last 15,000 years, the mountainous region from northern Norway to Scotland and the west of Ireland has risen by 1,000 to 1,300 feet (300 to 400 m). The uplift of the land has produced many high, sheer westward-facing cliffs where coastlines have been exposed to the pounding surf of the Atlantic Ocean.

Erosion

Sea cliffs are eroded by waves and by water running down the cliff face from the landward side. In cold climates the freeze-thaw action of water can split apart rocks on a cliff face. Large waves can generate pressure as great as 3 tons per square foot (30 tonnes per sq m). Erosion can be very speedy, cutting into the seaward edge of the land at up to 3 feet (1 m) or so each year.

Waves only reach a certain height up the cliffs even at high tide. However, they can have a devastating effect on the whole cliff face. The wave action can cut a horizontal slit or nick into the base of the sea cliff. The rock above has no support and therefore collapses.

The rate at which cliffs are eroded and weathered depends mainly on their geology (the type of rocks from which they are made) and on their structure. Igneous (IG-nee-uhs) rocks are

generally hard. They are formed when hot molten rock from inside Earth cools and hardens. Volcanic ash and dust layers are very soft, however, and easily eroded. Metamorphic (MEH-tuh-MAWR-fik) rocks (those that have been changed by great heat and pressure) are also generally strong and hard. Sedimentary (SEH-duh-MEN-tuh-ree) rocks form when small pieces of rock are laid down in layers. Sedimentary rocks, such as clays and shales, are often easily eroded. Some, such as quartzites, contain few lines of weakness. Whatever the type of rock, those with wide joints and splits allow water to get in and chemically and physically weather the rock. On coasts, waves can exert pressure within such rocks. Boulders can also fall into widened joints and exert even more pressure.

On the west coast of Ireland, the famous cliffs of Moher face the full force of the Atlantic Ocean. These cliffs are made of flat-lying layers of resistant sedimentary rocks laid down over 300 million years ago. The rocks resist erosion and therefore retreat slowly.

In contrast, the south coast of England and the white cliffs of Normandy in France are made of much softer chalk or limestone. This rock contains many joints and cracks, so the waves undercut it more quickly. Cliff falls often take place in these areas. California's Pacific coast also has very unstable cliffs. The region is made up of soft sedimentary rocks containing many cracks and also some rock layers that absorb water. The

The effects of cliff erosion can be devastating.

rocks that soak up rainwater collapse frequently, as the water in the rock causes chemical and physical changes that weaken the rock. Whole sections of cliff fall into a jumbled mass at the base. If the collapsed rock is removed by the sea, the whole process may be repeated.

Inland cliffs

Cliffs may form inland where rivers cut deep channels through the surface rock. This results in steep-sided gorges and canyons. The Grand Canyon, for example, has high cliffs formed by the Colorado River cutting down through horizontal layers of sedimentary rocks. In western Crete, the Samaria Gorge has been eroded considerably by the Tarraios River.

Glaciation leaves vertical cliffs in many places. When a valley glacier retreats, the valley sides have vertical cliff faces many hundreds of feet high. The Norwegian fjords are examples of such glaciation. Cliffs are also produced in corries or cirques (SUHRKS; deep, steep-walled basins on a mountain, usually forming the blunt end of a valley) by smaller glaciers. These cliffs are the result of glacial erosion and freeze-thaw action in the rock joints.

CHECK THESE OUT!
✔CANYON ✔COAST ✔EROSION ✔GEOLOGY
✔LANDFORM ✔MOUNTAIN ✔ROCK ✔WAVES

Climate

The regular pattern of weather that a region experiences over a long period is called its climate. Climate is not the same as weather. In many parts of the world, the weather can change very quickly, as clouds roll in bringing rain or the skies clear and the Sun breaks through. A description of a region's climate provides a much more general picture, a summing-up of all the weather conditions that have been observed in the area over a number of years.

The climate of a region influences the landscape and the local wildlife. It affects what species of animals live in the area and what plants can grow. Climate also influences human life in the region. It affects, for example, the kind of houses people build and the clothes they wear.

What affects climate?

Different parts of the world have very different climates. The regions immediately on either side of the equator (ih-KWAY-tuhr; an imaginary circle around Earth at equal distances from the North and South Poles) are hot and wet all year round. The polar regions are always cold. Around the world, climate depends on a number of different factors (influences). The most important factors are how close a region is to the equator, how high it is, and how near the sea.

Latitude and sunlight

Latitude (how far a region is from the equator) is one of the most important factors influencing climate. A region's latitude affects how much energy from sunlight it receives. At the equator, the Sun shines directly overhead. This means the Sun's rays are more intense, making it very hot.

North and south of the equator, Earth's surface curves away. The Sun's rays are spread out over a wider area so they become less powerful. At the polar regions, the rays are spread over a very wide area. They also have farther to travel through Earth's atmosphere, which weakens their effect still more, which is why the North and South Poles are so cold.

Tilt of the earth

For part of each year, the polar regions receive no sunlight at all. This is because Earth is tilted on its axis (the imaginary rod around which it rotates). As Earth moves around the Sun, one pole tilts toward the Sun, and the other tilts away. The region tilted toward the Sun is bathed in weak sunlight for long periods of the day. The region tilted away experiences long hours of darkness. Many other parts of Earth experience seasonal changes as a result of Earth's tilt.

Reflecting sunlight

The climate of a region is also affected by the nature of its surface. Different surfaces reflect varying amounts of the Sun's heat. Scientists call this the albedo (al-BEE-doh; reflective power) of a surface. For example, snow reflects back into space up to 95 percent of the sunlight it receives.

HIGHLIGHTS

◆ Climate is the regular weather pattern an area experiences over time.

◆ A region's climate is influenced by many different factors, including its distance from the equator, its altitude, and whether it is near to the sea.

◆ Winds, ocean currents, and the surface of Earth also affect climate.

◆ Different parts of Earth have very different climates. Climate experts identify 12 major climate zones, plus a highland zone, that differ in terms of temperatures and rainfall.

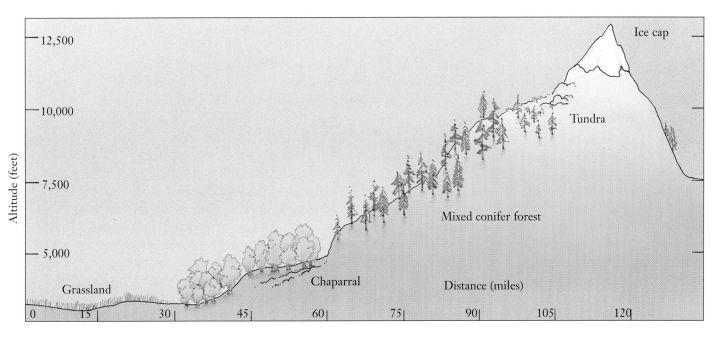

Altitude (feet)

12,500

10,000

7,500

5,000

Ice cap

Tundra

Mixed conifer forest

Grassland

Chaparral

Distance (miles)

0   15   30   45   60   75   90   105   120

Climate and vegetation vary with altitude.

Sandy deserts reflect only 25 percent of the Sun's heat and absorb the rest, making them very hot.

Altitude

Altitude (how high an area is above sea level) is another major influence on climate. High mountain areas are much cooler than low-lying regions. This is because the air is thinner at high altitudes and therefore less able to absorb the Sun's heat. Therefore high mountains, even on the equator, are covered with ice and snow all year round. The climate also affects the vegetation that grows on the upper and lower slopes of the mountain.

Oceans

The oceans are the third major influence on climate. In regions near the oceans, called maritime or marine regions, temperatures do not vary as much as they do far inland. This is because the water temperature, which affects the temperature of the air above it, changes much more slowly than the temperature of the land.

Ocean currents also have a warming or cooling influence on climate. The Gulf Stream is a warm current that flows northeast from the Gulf of Mexico across the Atlantic to the shores of western Europe. Britain and other countries lie at about the same latitude as Newfoundland, but the current makes the climate of western Europe much warmer than that of eastern Canada. The Japanese Current has a cooling influence on nearby shores and flows southward down the north Pacific coast of Canada and the United States.

Inland, large bodies of water such as lakes and land-locked seas can also influence the local climate. In the United States, the Great Lakes affect the long-term weather of the surrounding area. In winter, clouds passing over the lakes absorb extra moisture that produces heavy snowfalls along southern shores. These blizzards are called lake-effect snowstorms. The prevailing winds also affect a region's climate.

New Zealand is so isolated that its climate remains unchanged by weather from elsewhere.

Climate zones

Climatologists are scientists who study climate. Modern climatologists identify 12 major climate zones around the world, plus a highland zone. The zones are distinguished by their average temperatures and the rainfall they receive.

The regions around the equator are called the tropics. They experience a tropical climate, with high temperatures all year round. Some parts of the tropics have what scientists call a tropical wet climate. These areas experience humid (moist) conditions. Torrential rain falls nearly every afternoon. Much of the land is covered by dense rain forest. Other parts of the tropics have a dry season and a rainy season.

North and south of the tropics lie the subtropics. The climate there is somewhat cooler than in the tropics, with warm to hot summers and cooler winters. Some parts of the subtropics experience moderate rainfall all year round. Other parts have dry summers.

Broadly north or south of the subtropics, temperate regions have a moderate climate, with warm summers and cool winters. In some areas, rain falls all year round; in regions with a Mediterranean climate, summers are dry. Areas near coasts have a marine climate, with cool summers. Inland regions have what scientists call a continental climate. Temperatures there are more extreme than on coasts, with warmer summers or cooler winters.

The subarctic region lies north of temperate lands in the Northern Hemisphere. Subarctic summers are brief and cool, and winters are cold and long. The region is covered mainly with dense forests of conifer trees. Beyond the forests lie the barren, treeless lands called the tundra.

The polar regions in the far north and south of Earth experience icy weather all year round. The land is covered with a permanent ice cap up to 2½ miles (4 km) thick, and no plants grow.

Deserts are areas in any part of the world where very little or no rain falls each year. Some deserts are scorching hot by day and freezing at night; high deserts are cold all the time.

The map below shows where the world's major climate zones are located.

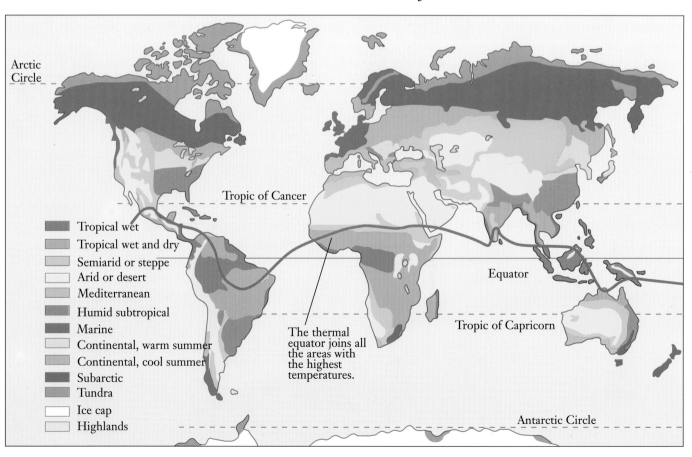

Arctic Circle

Tropic of Cancer

Equator

Tropic of Capricorn

Antarctic Circle

Tropical wet
Tropical wet and dry
Semiarid or steppe
Arid or desert
Mediterranean
Humid subtropical
Marine
Continental, warm summer
Continental, cool summer
Subarctic
Tundra
Ice cap
Highlands

The thermal equator joins all the areas with the highest temperatures.

LOOK CLOSER

Volcanoes and Climate

Volcanic eruptions can affect Earth's climate. In 1815, the largest eruption ever recorded occurred at Mount Tambora in Indonesia. The volcano spewed enormous quantities of dust, ash, and lava into the atmosphere. Nearby regions were plunged into a dusk that lasted for three days. A giant cloud of volcanic debris from Tambora spread throughout the upper atmosphere, shadowing Earth's surface for more than a year. This affected the amount of sunlight that reached Earth's surface. The following year was called "the year without a summer." Around the world, growing seasons were shorter and many crops failed.

The more recent eruptions of Mount St. Helens in Washington State in 1980 and El Chinchonal in Mexico in 1982 also threw huge quantities of fine ash into the upper atmosphere. This ash can stay aloft for years, reflecting the Sun's rays back into space and cooling the climate around the world.

Climate change

On both a global and a regional scale, Earth's climate seems to stay the same. However, it actually changes slowly and was very different in the past. Long, cold periods called ice ages were interspersed with warmer periods. Scientists prove this by looking at evidence left behind in the ice caps that still exist on Earth.

Scientists find out about Earth's climate in the past by studying ice that was formed at the time. They drill into ice-containing glaciers that were formed thousands of years ago in order to collect samples called ice cores. Scientists can find out the age of ice cores using the technique of radiocarbon dating. The dated ice can then be analyzed to provide information on the blend of gases in the atmosphere, temperature, and snowfall in the distant past.

Most climate experts believe that Earth's climate is changing quite quickly at present and getting warmer. This change is called global warming. Many people are worried that global warming is being caused by human activity. Evidence suggests that pollution from automobiles and other vehicles, burning the rain forests, and increasing industrialization around the world are changing the balance of gases in Earth's atmosphere. The atmosphere is now trapping more of the Sun's heat, which leads to a general warming. This change is called the greenhouse effect because the gases in Earth's atmosphere trap heat in much the same way as the glass in a greenhouse does.

Climate experts predict that these rising temperatures around the world will cause sea levels to rise as the ice caps of the polar regions melt. Rainfall, winds, and ocean currents may also become more variable, causing widespread climate change. Governments must now work to reach agreement on how to reduce the pollution levels that are causing global warming.

CHECK THESE OUT!
✔GLOBAL WARMING ✔ICE AGE ✔POLAR REGION
✔RADIOCARBON DATING ✔SEASON
✔WEATHER ✔WIND

Iceberg chunks stranded on a rocky beach in Alaska. They remain whole due to the cold climate.

Cloud

Visible mass of moisture floating in the air

Clouds are made of millions of tiny water droplets or ice crystals, so small and light that they can float. Clouds signal changes in the weather and also play a part in influencing Earth's long-term climate. They come in different shapes and colors and form at different heights in the air.

The atmosphere is the blanket of air that surrounds Earth. Earth's atmosphere is made up mainly of oxygen and nitrogen. It also contains tiny amounts of other gases, including moisture in the form of water vapor, an invisible gas.

Earth's atmosphere is made up of different layers or regions. The layer closest to Earth is called the troposphere (TROH-puh-SFIR). The troposphere contains nearly all the atmosphere's water vapor. Clouds form and most of the world's weather happens in this region.

How clouds form

Clouds form when air laden with water vapor rises upward. Air cools as it rises, and cool air holds less water vapor than warm air. As the water vapor rises and cools, some of it turns into droplets of water or ice crystals. This process is

Different cloud formations are linked with various kinds of weather. Cumulus clouds can bring rain.

called condensation. The droplets or crystals gather together to form clouds.

The air in the troposphere is not all the same. Huge bodies of air called air masses form over the land or ocean. They may contain warm or cold, moist or dry air. Clouds often form where a mass of warm air meets a mass of cold air. The region where these air masses collide is called a weather front.

Inside a cloud the droplets of water and ice crystals are so small and light that they move slowly, swirling in the air like smoke. However, when air laden with moisture cools beyond a certain point (the dew point), the air becomes saturated (it cannot hold any more water vapor). The droplets join up to make larger droplets. These become too heavy to float in the air, so they fall as rain. At lower temperatures, the moisture in the cloud falls as sleet, snow, or hail.

Air cools, beginning the condensation process, because it rises. Clouds may be pushed upward by the Sun's heat radiating off the warm surface of the land or sea. A mass of warm air may be forced upward by cooler air moving in below.

HIGHLIGHTS

♦ Clouds are made of moisture in the air in the form of water vapor, water droplets, or ice crystals.

♦ Clouds are classified according to their height in the atmosphere, as low, medium, or high clouds.

♦ The names of clouds are taken from Latin words that describe their appearance.

♦ The movement, shape, and height of clouds are linked with different kinds of weather. Thus clouds help scientists to predict the weather.

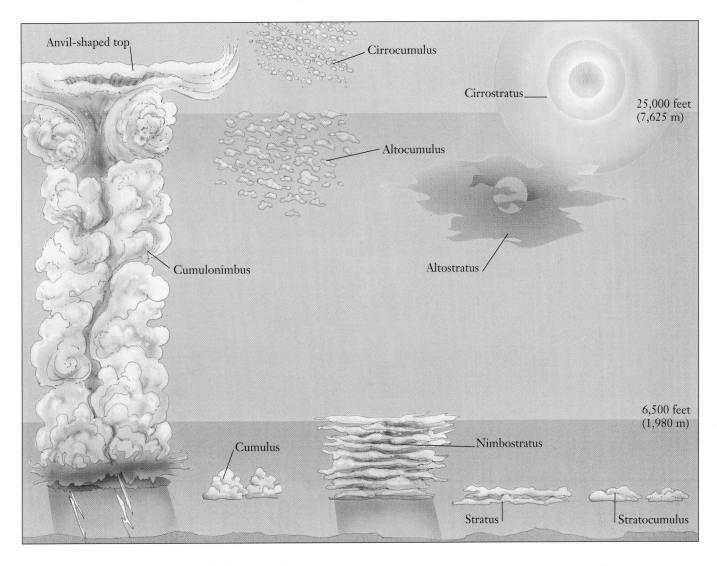

Anvil-shaped top

Cirrocumulus

Cirrostratus

25,000 feet
(7,625 m)

Altocumulus

Cumulonimbus

Altostratus

6,500 feet
(1,980 m)

Cumulus

Nimbostratus

Stratus

Stratocumulus

Alternatively, air may be pushed upward as it meets the slope of a mountain. Whatever the cause, the result is the same: precipitation, in the form of rain, sleet, snow, or hail, followed by colder weather and showers or thunderstorms. A warm front forms when the leading edge of a mass of warm air slides slowly over a mass of cold air. Warm fronts move more slowly than cold fronts. They bring warmer temperatures but also storms or steady light rain.

Identifying clouds

Clouds are classified according to the height at which they form in the atmosphere. Scientists who study Earth's atmosphere divide the troposphere into three levels: low, medium, and high. Low clouds form from ground level to 6,500 feet (1,980 m). Middle clouds form between 6,500 feet and 25,000 feet (1,980 m and

The different types of cloud are classified according to their shape and the height at which they form.

7,625 m). High clouds form above 25,000 feet (7,625 m). The movement, shape, and height of the different cloud types are linked with different kinds of weather. Thus, clouds help scientists to predict the weather over the next hours or days.

High clouds

Cirrus (SIHR-uhs) clouds are one of the main types of high clouds. These feathery clouds are mainly made up of ice crystals. Sometimes the wind blows them into hairlike shapes called mares' tails. Cirrus clouds do not usually bring rain, but mares' tails may signify distant storms.

Cirrostratus (SIHR-oh-STRAY-tuhs) clouds are also high clouds. They often form a white veil covering all or part of the sky but are too thin to

Ice only

Mixed ice and water

Water only

The distribution of ice and water in a towering cumulonimbus cloud.

mask the Sun. The name *cirrostratus* comes from the Latin word *stratum*, which means cover. Cirrostratus clouds are also made of ice crystals. Sometimes they produce a circular rainbow called a halo around the Sun. Many people believe this is a sign that rain will follow. Certainly, when cirrostratus clouds thicken, rain usually falls later the same day.

Cirrocumulus (SIHR-oh-KYOO-myuh-luhs) clouds are the third main type of high cloud. Their name comes from the Latin word *cumulus*, which means pile. Cirrocumulus are white, thin, grainy, and rippled clouds. They create an effect called a mackerel sky because the pattern is similar to the rippling marks on a mackerel's back. Cirrocumulus clouds usually come before a warm front, which is the leading edge of a mass of warm air that pushes cold air out of the way. When they thicken as a storm approaches, they become cirrostratus clouds and their ripples develop into towers and turrets.

A bank of altocumulus seen from above, lit up and colored by a sunset.

Middle clouds

Middle clouds are altostratus (AL-toh-STRAY-tuhs) and altocumulus (AL-toh-KYOO-myuh-luhs) clouds. *Alto* comes from the Latin word for high or upper air. Altostratus clouds are uniform blue- or gray-tinged sheets of clouds that cover all or part of the sky. They are made of water vapor, ice, raindrops, or snowflakes, and are thin enough to vaguely reveal the Sun.

Altocumulus clouds are usually evenly spaced mounds of white and gray cloudlets that look like cotton wool balls. Sometimes they appear as a large sheet of clouds or they may be arranged in parallel lines. Altocumulus clouds are a sign of unsettled weather to come.

Low clouds

There are three main types of low clouds: stratus (STRAY-tuhs), nimbostratus, and stratocumulus clouds. Stratus clouds are low-lying, uniformly gray clouds that produce drizzle and snow. Often they are dense enough to mask the Sun. A rising ground-level fog can produce stratus clouds.

Nimbostratus are dark-gray, moisture-bearing clouds. They occur in a layer thick enough to block out the Sun. These clouds can produce steady rain or snow, but not a thunderstorm.

Stratocumulus clouds are layers of puffy white or gray clouds that may have dark patches. They are usually made of water droplets except in very cold weather.

LOOK CLOSER

Humanmade Clouds

As well as clouds that form naturally, humanmade clouds are also sometimes seen in the sky. They do not produce rain, hail, or snow, but they may show climate change or pollution. Contrails are clouds triggered by the condensation trails of high-flying jet planes. Sometimes when aircraft fly overhead, their hot exhaust gases mix with the cold air to form streaks of cirrus clouds that mark where the plane flew. Sometimes contrails gradually spread across the sky, changing a clear day into one with a layer of thin cloud.

Nacreous (NAY-kree-uhs) clouds form in northern skies above the troposphere, in a region of the atmosphere where there is no water vapor. At night, these shimmering clouds become luminous (glow). For many years, they puzzled cloud observers. Now researchers believe they are made mainly of methane, a gas released by mining and industrial processes. Methane is also produced naturally by cattle, termites, swamps, and rice paddies.

Vertical clouds

Vertical clouds span the different layers of the troposphere. They may reach heights of 40,000 feet (12 km) or higher. Cumulus clouds are dense, fluffy, and often clearly outlined. They develop vertically as rising mounds, towers, or domes. Sometimes the bulging upper part of a cumulus cloud resembles a cauliflower in shape.

In sunlight, cumulus clouds look brilliant white. Their bases are smooth, nearly level, and relatively dark. They are dark because little sunlight can penetrate the cloud to light the base. Cumulus clouds may produce rain showers.

Darker, heavier cumulus clouds are called cumulonimbus or thunderheads. These clouds reach altitudes of at least 40,000 to 60,000 feet (12 to 18 km) as they grow upward in the atmosphere. They contain not only water droplets and ice crystals, but also large raindrops, snowflakes, and hailstones, or grainy pellets of ice. Cumulonimbus clouds may have tops that resemble towers, mountains, or anvils. They are linked with lightning, thunder, and hail.

Weather satellites

On April 1, 1960, the view of the world's weather changed forever when the first U.S. weather satellite was launched. The satellite was named TIROS, short for Television and Infrared Observation Satellite. It opened up a new age of worldwide cooperation in weather forecasting.

Before weather satellites, individual countries could produce forecasts based only on information gathered inside their own borders. The weather was observed over less than one-fifth of the globe. Today, most places on Earth have a satellite within range every two hours, giving information ranging from storms to volcanic activity. Weather satellites give detailed information on clouds, providing photographs for the weather forecasts on TV. Satellites provide information on the density, height, and movement of clouds around the world, adding to the data obtained from land-based instruments. As the tools and techniques of weather observation become more sophisticated, meteorologists, who study the weather, learn to make ever-more accurate predictions.

CHECK THESE OUT!
✔ATMOSPHERE ✔CLIMATE ✔LIGHTNING AND THUNDER ✔RAIN, SLEET, AND SNOW ✔WEATHER

Coal

A fossil fuel that is an important source of industrial energy

Coal was once the most important fuel in the world. During the Industrial Revolution of the 18th and 19th centuries it was essential for the huge manufacturing industries that sprang up, and it powered steam engines of all kinds across the globe. Until well into the 20th century, coal was also used to provide energy for electricity generators, as a source of household gas, and as the raw material for many chemical industries. Now other sources of energy, such as oil, natural gas, and nuclear power, are also used.

Like oil and natural gas, coal is a fossil fuel. It is a kind of rock that is composed of at least 50 percent carbon-containing material, which will burn. The carbon comes from ancient plant remains that have been compressed over millions of years. Coal has been formed in different periods of Earth's history, beginning about 360 million years ago. The first period, which lasted some 74 million years, is called the Carboniferous (coal-bearing) period for this reason. Most of the world's coal deposits were formed during this time.

The Carboniferous period is usually divided into the Pennsylvanian and Mississippian periods. The vast Appalachian coalfields, extending from Pennsylvania to northeast Alabama, date from the Pennsylvanian period. Coal beds under the Rocky Mountains are around 100 million years old. More recent coal beds that are around 65 million years old are found in Wyoming, Montana, and in the Gulf Coastal Plain of Texas. The world's reserves of coal are calculated at more than 600 billion tons (544 billion tonnes). In terms of the amount of heat this represents, coal reserves are around 22 times greater than the reserves of oil and natural gas combined.

Coal is a valuable fuel because of its carbon content. However, there is very little carbon present as the element. Most of it is in the form of complex compounds of carbon and hydrogen (hydrocarbons), which burn easily in air. Coal also contains varying amounts of oxygen, nitrogen, and sulfur, as well as other minerals.

Although it was originally burned directly as fuel, most coal mined today is changed into coke. This process is called destructive distillation. The coal is heated in huge ovens, without air, to a temperature ranging from 1300°F to 2200°F

Coal reserves are greater than those of oil and natural gas, the other fossil fuels.

HIGHLIGHTS

◆ Coal is a rock, formed from plant remains that have undergone intense heating, buried deep underground for millions of years.

◆ Heating coal without air produces coke, coal tar, and coal gas.

◆ Coal was first used on a large scale as an energy source during the Industrial Revolution of the 18th and 19th centuries. It is still a major source of energy throughout the world.

◆ Coal is the most abundant fossil fuel.

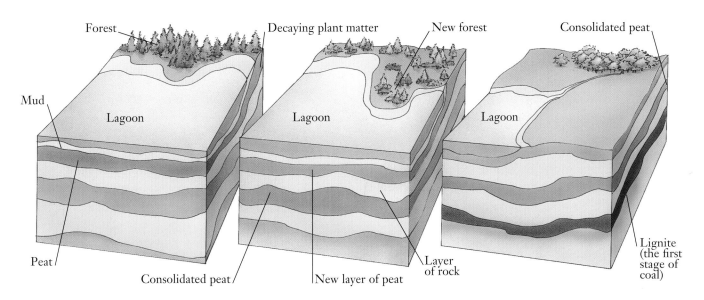

Forest — Decaying plant matter — New forest — Consolidated peat

Mud — Lagoon — Lagoon — Lagoon

Peat — Consolidated peat — New layer of peat — Layer of rock — Lignite (the first stage of coal)

The formation of coal takes millions of years. It first takes the form of peat, then becomes coal with the effects of pressure and heat.

(704°C to 1204°C). The coal is broken down into coal gas and coal tar to leave coke. The coke is used for smelting iron ore, which produces iron, and some coke is also burned as fuel in power plants.

Coal gas

Coal gas is made up mostly of hydrogen, methane, and carbon monoxide. Each of these gases burns readily in air, forming water and carbon dioxide. Carbon monoxide is highly poisonous to humans. It binds to molecules in the blood that normally carry oxygen to the tissues and the brain. In the past, coal gas supplied for household use was responsible for many suicides and accidental deaths.

Household gas has now been almost entirely replaced by natural gas, which does not contain carbon monoxide. For over a century, however, coal gas was used for lighting and heating in many parts of the world. The first use was in the 18th century to light a castle in Germany. In 1792, inventor William Murdock developed a gas jet and fed coal gas through iron pipes to light his cottage and the offices of a factory. In Britain the Gas, Light & Coke Company, formed in 1812, became the first public utility in the world to supply gas for households.

Coal tar

As well as coal gas, the intense heat of the coke oven also drives off coal tar, which is cooled and collected. Coal tar is a mixture of many different hydrocarbons, which can be separated by the process of distillation. The individual compounds, such as benzene, toluene, and naphthalene, became the starting-point of the organic chemistry industry in the second half of the 19th century. Without these hydrocarbons, there would not be many of the drugs, plastics, and other synthetic (humanmade) substances that are important today. After the available hydrocarbons have been distilled from the coal tar, what remains is used for road surfacing.

Coal mining

Coal deposits are found in layers, called seams or measures, at different depths below Earth's surface. These seams vary in thickness and structure. Because of the way in which they were formed by the pressure of sediment above them, they are found within layers of rock such as sandstone or shale.

There are three ways of reaching these coal seams. One is to sink deep underground mines with shafts and connecting tunnels. Explosives are used to open up the seams. A crew of people then uses digging machines to extract the coal, taking care to ensure that the shafts and tunnels do not collapse. Usually, nearly half the available coal must be left in place to provide support and to prevent later subsidence (sinking). A different method that has been used, particularly in Russia, is to set fire to the coal underground. The heat can be used directly for powering electricity generators and domestic heating, and the other products can be collected and distilled.

The second way of getting coal is by strip mining. This is an economical way of mining the coal nearest the surface. The disadvantage of this method is the serious environmental damage caused by the wide destruction of surface areas.

The third method is auger (AW-guhr) mining, which has developed in the last 50 years. Machines drill horizontal holes, up to 7 feet (2 m) in diameter, into the coal seams. Explosives are not needed to open up the seams, and only a small crew is needed to operate the machines.

Power stations require vast quantities of coal, which is often transported to the stations by rail.

LOOK CLOSER

Coal Formation

The prehistoric plants such as giant trees and ferns that were changed into coal once grew on the edges of vast subtropical swamps. As these plants died, they fell into the water and slowly decayed. Later, the surface of Earth sank, and a sediment of mud settled on top. The pressure changed the plant remains into peat, a spongy material that is still used as fuel in parts of the world, particularly in Ireland.

The formation of coal takes millions of years. Coal forms when plant matter is heated by being buried deep underground. This heating drives off some of the plant materials, such as water, leaving behind the carbon content. Therefore as the plant matter continued to sink, the pressure and heat increased. Gradually the peat changed into lignite (LIG-NYT), the first stage of coal. Further pressure and heat continued to make the coal gradually become harder.

Coal is classified according to its rank, that is, how much it has altered from the original plant material. As coal increases in rank, its value as a fuel increases. The commonest type of coal is bituminous (buh-TYOO-muh-nuhs) coal, in which the original plant material has been almost completely transformed. It burns easily and produces heat very efficiently. The highest ranking coal is anthracite (AN-thruh-SYT). Anthracite is less common than lower ranking coals, but it is valuable because it produces very little smoke when it burns.

Environmental effects

The chemical makeup of coal is responsible for harmful environmental effects when it is used as a source of energy. Burning coal produces a large amount of carbon dioxide. Many scientists think that this gas contributes to the greenhouse effect (the gradual warming of Earth's atmosphere). In addition, coal is a major cause of acid rain. The sulfur and nitrogen in coal are released as oxides as the coal burns. These are changed into sulfuric and nitrous acids, resulting in acid rain.

CHECK THESE OUT!

✔CARBON ✔FOSSIL ✔GLOBAL WARMING
✔MINING ✔NATURAL GAS ✔OIL

Coast
The boundary zone between the land and the oceans

The boundaries between land and sea have changed greatly over the course of millions of years. Earth's surface has moved many times, being forced upward in some places and sinking in others. The level of water in the oceans has also changed. Up to 10,000 years ago much of the northern hemisphere was covered with ice. As the ice melted, the sea level rose as much as 400 feet (122 m). Other changes to coastlines continue to take place. Erosion by the sea carries the land away, depositing it elsewhere as sand or rock debris (duh-BREE; broken pieces).

Geologists now know that the major changes in Earth's crust have been caused by the gradual movement of gigantic areas of crust called tectonic plates. The Atlantic Ocean was formed as the landmass that is now the American continent moved away from what is now Europe and Africa.

Types of coasts can be classified according to the way in which they have been formed. The coasts of whole continents were formed either by the separation of two tectonic plates or by one driving against another. The east coast of

Some high, rugged coasts are produced when a whole area of land is pushed upward.

HIGHLIGHTS

♦ Coastlines were first formed by the movement of giant areas of Earth's crust called tectonic plates.

♦ Melting ice at the end of the ice age caused ocean levels to rise as much as 400 feet (122 m).

♦ Later shaping of coastlines was due mainly to the effects of waves and currents.

♦ Coastal protection can create as many problems as it prevents.

North America is an example of tectonic plate separation. High, rugged coasts are produced by the collision of two plates.

Coastal change was also caused by the ice that once covered the northern hemisphere. In places, its weight caused the land beneath to sink. As the ice melted, the crust rose again. Some beaches that sank beneath the weight of the ice are now hundreds of feet above sea level. In other places, such as Chesapeake Bay, the land remained flooded, forming deep bays and river estuaries.

Coastal Pollution

For many centuries, humans have used the rivers and the oceans as places to dump their waste products. Now the oceans are reaching their limit for absorbing waste. The health of many living organisms is at risk, including the animals that live in coastal waters, humans who eat seafood, and those who use coastal waters for work or pleasure. In addition, the increasing number of people who live close to the coast has had a marked effect on shoreline pollution.

Estuaries and wetlands are the ocean's first line of defense against pollution. Their ecology (relationship between the environment and its living organisms) exists in a fragile balance. Between 1940 and 1980, the number of Americans living within 50 miles (80 km) of the Atlantic and Pacific coasts and the Gulf of Mexico more than doubled, and it continues to increase. Development of coastal areas means that at least half of the nation's estuaries and wetlands no longer exist to filter pollution from the land. This reduction has had a dramatic effect on the levels of pollution now found in coastal environments.

The advancing glaciers of the last ice age also carved out deep U-shaped valleys in mountain rocks. When the glaciers melted and sea levels rose, these valleys flooded. Examples can be seen in the fjords of Norway.

The effects of waves and tides depend on the geological nature of the coasts. Hard rocks resist erosion better than softer materials. Steep, nearly vertical cliffs expose only a few inches of the underlying structure between high and low tides. Flat coasts may have more than a mile exposed to wave action between the tides.

Erosion and deposition

Along some coasts, the faulting (fracture and shift of rocks that lie side by side) between different strata (STRA-tuh; layers) of rocks has formed almost straight cliffs. Here, sections of resistant rock, such as granite, remain as the weaker rock around them is eroded by wave action. Eventually these hard rocks remain standing above the sea surface as arches, caves, or stacks (columns of rock).

Other coastal features formed in the same way include headlands (high, broad areas sticking out to sea), points (narrower, sharp-ended pieces of land), and peninsulas, which are areas almost entirely surrounded by water and joined to the mainland by narrow necks, called isthmuses (IS-muhs-ez). Sometimes wave erosion produces platforms, gently sloping surfaces that extend from the base of a cliff. Tectonic movement or changes in sea level may submerge or expose these platforms above sea level.

Erosion is not the only factor to reshape a coast. Waves, tides, and currents can have an effect by depositing sediments. First, boulders

Wide, sandy beaches often support the growth of vegetation such as grasses.

and pebbles are deposited when waves erode a rocky cliff. Gradually, wave action breaks down the pebbles into sand. Where the coastline is made of relatively soft, easily broken material, the eroded ground may be carried away by the water, leaving behind small bays.

In the southeastern and southern United States, wide sandy beaches and smooth plains of loose sediment are commonly found. Inland from such beaches, dunes (DOONZ) are often formed. Dunes are soft hills or ridges of sand heaped up by the wind. Sandy beaches usually slope gently, with a wide foreshore between high and low tides. At the back of the foreshore may be one or two berms (BAHRMZ; horizontal areas of material deposited during high tides or storms).

Sometimes the movement of currents builds sand bars or barrier islands parallel to the coast. Barrier islands are much larger than sand bars and are built up in ridges and frequently support vegetation. On the landward side, swampy terraces extend into a shallow lagoon, which separates the barrier from the main shore.

Sediment from large rivers such as the Mississippi can also result in considerable areas of deposition at their mouths. These areas are called deltas and are often triangular in shape.

Waves

Waves are swells or ridges of water that move across the surface of the sea. They are caused by the drag of the wind on the water so that the energy of motion is transferred from the air to the sea. The amount of energy contained by the waves depends on three factors: the speed of the wind, how long the wind blows, and the distance over which the wind has acted on the water.

Large, powerful waves cause most coastal erosion. During violent storms, whole beaches can be stripped of their sediments, which are then deposited below the zone where the waves are breaking. Later, smaller waves will often carry the sediments back to the beaches.

If the direction of the wave crests is at an angle to the shoreline, the waves will cause a current to run parallel to the shore. This current can carry off sediment for long distances. The sediment can form new coastal features such as spits, which are long ridges of sand or gravel extending from the land, particularly where the coastline turns a corner. Natural and human-made structures both block this movement.

Coastal protection

A natural form of coastal protection is provided by the coral reefs attached to island or mainland shores. Barrier islands also help to reduce the energy of waves reaching the shoreline.

Where building development has come close to the shoreline, humanmade coastal protection is necessary to prevent further beach and cliff erosion. This protection can create problems of its own. For example, groins may be built out from the shore to trap sand that is being moved along the coast. This sand deposit widens and protects the beach. However, increased erosion down-coast of a groin usually equals the volume of sand retained by the groin.

Jetties can be built at the entrance to a river or inlet to stabilize the entrance channel. They can also have the same effect as groins. Breakwaters are much bigger structures, often extending into relatively deep water to protect a shoreline or harbor entrance.

CHECK THESE OUT!
✔CLIFF ✔EROSION ✔ICE AGE ✔PLATE TECTONICS
✔RIVER ✔TIDAL WAVE ✔TIDE ✔WAVES

Color

The perception of different wavelengths of light visible to the human eye

A light spectrum created by a glass prism.

Color is something that some animals see, either as colored light or when light is reflected by a colored object. Light is electromagnetic radiation, which consists of waves of energy that move through empty space at 186,282 miles per second (299,792 km/s). The distance between the crests of two waves is called the wavelength. Electromagnetic wavelengths can vary from more than 50 miles (80 km) to less than a trillionth of a meter.

Visible light has electromagnetic wavelengths between 760 and 380 billionths of a meter. (A billionth of a meter is called a nanometer, nm.) Radiation from the Sun in this range passes most easily through Earth's atmosphere. Therefore most life on Earth has evolved to be sensitive to visible light.

HIGHLIGHTS

♦ When a beam of white light is shone through a prism, it is split up into a complete range of colors, called a spectrum, from red at one end to violet at the other.

♦ Light is electromagnetic radiation that is visible and in a wavelength range between 760 and 380 nanometers.

♦ The eye contains three types of cone receptors that respond to different wavelength ranges.

♦ The color of an object depends on the wavelengths of light reflected from it.

♦ Colored light beams mix by addition. Mixed pigments get their color by subtraction.

The colors in white light

Sunlight looks white. English scientist Sir Isaac Newton (1642–1727) was the first person to shine a narrow beam of sunlight through a glass prism (PRIH-zuhm; a transparent body that separates the different colors in light). He found the sunlight was split into different colors, just like a rainbow. This range of colors is called the spectrum. When Newton shone the spectrum through a second, upside-down, prism, the colors combined again to give white light.

White light is therefore a mixture of colors. Although he was a scientist, Newton was also interested in magic. Seven is thought to be a magic number, so Newton named seven different colors in the spectrum: red, orange, yellow, green, blue, indigo, and violet. However, the colors of a rainbow in the sky or the spectrum from a prism blend into one another. In fact, the spectrum is made up of hundreds of different colors, each of which has its own wavelength.

The longest visible wavelengths are seen as red and the shortest are seen as violet. Radiation that is just beyond the red end of the spectrum is called infrared (*infra* means below.) Although humans cannot see infrared radiation, it can be felt as heat. Radiation with a shorter wavelength than violet is called ultraviolet (where *ultra* means beyond or above). Many insects can see ultraviolet light and make out patterns on flower petals that are invisible to humans.

When white light shines on an object, some of the wavelengths are absorbed and others are reflected. A red object, for example, absorbs all

LOOK CLOSER

How Substances Are Colored

Light exists as a series of waves of energy, but it can also be thought of as tiny packets of energy. These packets are called photons (FOH-tahnz). They arrive like a stream of particles. The amount of energy a photon carries is always the same for any particular wavelength.

An atom is made up of a nucleus surrounded by electrons. The electrons are in sets at different energy levels, and an electron can only move from one level to a higher level if it receives exactly the right amount of energy. An atom will absorb a photon if the amount of energy carried by the photon is exactly what is needed to raise an electron to a higher energy level. That is, the atom will absorb light of a particular wavelength.

Colored substances are made up of several atoms combined into molecules. The electron energy levels are changed but the molecule can still absorb only photons of particular energies. The molecule will absorb only certain colors. Wavelengths that are not absorbed are reflected or, in the case of transparent (see-through) materials, transmitted.

How the eye sees color

The central part of the eye's retina contains receptors called cones. Each one is sensitive to a different range of wavelengths. When light falls on these cones, they generate electric signals that are sent to the brain. The brain then combines these different signals to make up the color that humans can see.

There are three different types of cone receptors. One type is most sensitive to light of wavelengths between 450 and 490 nanometers (blue) and less sensitive to a range of colors extending into violet at one side and green at the other. A second type of cone responds best to

A rainbow is sunlight that has been split into a spectrum by raindrops.

wavelengths except those in the red end of the spectrum. The red light is reflected into the eye, which is why the object appears red. If a pure green or blue light is shone on a red object, there is no red to be reflected and therefore the object appears as black to the human eye. Transparent, colored objects get their color in a similar way. They absorb most of the wavelengths, letting just a narrow range of wavelengths through. Some transparent objects appear a very different color in reflected light than in transmitted light.

A colored light is generally a mixture of wavelengths within the color range that humans see. Light of just one wavelength is called monochromatic (meaning single color). Lasers, for example, produce monochromatic light of a fixed wavelength, and the yellow light of sodium-vapor streetlamps is also nearly monochromatic. That is why it is so difficult to judge the colors of cars in this type of street lighting.

light of wavelengths between 490 and 560 nanometers (green) but also detects some yellow and blue. The third type responds best to light between 560 and 590 nanometers (yellow) but also detects orange and red.

Some people are color blind, which is a hereditary condition (passed from parent to child). They cannot distinguish between two or more of the colors red, green, and blue because one or more of the types of cone receptors do not work properly.

Many other animals do not see colors in the range that humans do. Monkeys, apes, birds, and fish seem to be aware of different colors but most mammals are not. However, experimenters think cats can distinguish between certain colors. Many insects see color, although probably not in the same way as humans. Some insects have as many as 10 different color receptors in their eyes. Bees, for example, cannot see red but they can see ultraviolet light.

Mixing colors

U.S. industrialist Edwin L. Land (1909–1991), the inventor of the Polaroid camera, carried out many experiments with colored lights. He showed that an image projected in light of only two colors could be seen in a full range of colors. This suggests that the brain can fill in the other colors so that humans see what they expect to see. An important example of this is additive color mixing. If separate beams of red and green light are

Yellow, magenta, and cyan are the three primary colors of paints and pigments. They work by absorption. Each absorbs one of the primary colors of light and reflects the other two.

The three primary colors of light are red, green, and blue. When mixed together they produce a white light.

shone onto a screen, the area where they overlap is colored yellow. Beams of red, green, and blue overlap to look white. These three colors are therefore called additive primary colors.

The color produced by mixing any two primaries is called the complement of the third primary. Red and green light combine to give yellow, which is the complement of blue. Green and blue light combine to give a greenish-blue color called cyan (SY-an), the complement of red. Red and blue light combine to give magenta (muh-JEN-tuh), the complement of green.

Mixing paints or inks containing colored pigments has the opposite effect. Mixing yellow and blue paints gives green. Red and yellow give orange, red and blue give violet, and red and green give dark brown. This effect is called subtraction. It works even better if the colors are magenta, yellow, and cyan, the subtractive primaries. Different amounts of magenta and yellow give red and orange, yellow and cyan give green, and magenta and cyan give blue and violet. This is because each pigment absorbs (or subtracts) all colors except its own. The brain then recognizes all the colors in between.

This is used as the principle of printing in color. The colored image is broken down into dots or small areas of magenta, yellow, and cyan. Depending on the size of each dot or the amount of colored ink in each area, the brain sees a complete range of colors. Usually, however, even a complete overlap of magenta, yellow, and cyan does not produce a true black. So black ink must also be used to define shadows and the completely black areas. If you look at a colored printed image with a magnifier, you will be able to see the individual dots.

Television, on the other hand, uses additive colors. The image on a television screen is also made up of tiny dots, which glow when they are struck by an electron beam. Each dot sends out either red, green, or blue light. At a distance, the signals that the eye sends to the brain produce an image in a full range of colors.

Color photography makes use of a combination of additive and subtractive color. Color film usually consists of three different layers. The top layer absorbs only blue. The second layer can absorb both blue and green, but a layer of yellow dye is placed above it to filter out any blue that has not been absorbed. The bottom layer is sensitive to most colors but, by the time light reaches it, everything except red has been filtered out.

When the film is processed, each layer is dyed with subtractive dyes. In the photograph, a blue sky is dyed with cyan and some magenta; green grass is dyed with both cyan and yellow; and a red dress is dyed with yellow and magenta. A color negative film, however, is dyed with complementary colors instead. Red becomes greenish-blue, blue becomes yellow, and green becomes magenta. When a positive print is made, it is like taking another color photograph of this negative.

Classifying colors

Colors are described by three qualities: hue (HYEW), saturation, and intensity (luminance). Hue describes the color in terms of its

This color wheel shows the primary colors red, blue, and yellow. Their secondary colors are placed between them.

wavelength. Saturation is a measure of the depth of a color, that is, the amount of white that is mixed with it. The more that a color approaches white, the paler it gets, the less saturated it is. Intensity is used to describe the brightness of a color.

To help mix and match colors, artists, printers, and paint scientists sometimes use a color wheel. In its simplest form, this has three primary colors at equal distances around the circle. Between each two primaries are the secondary colors that are made by mixing them. In this way, each color appears opposite its complement. A more complex wheel, such as the Munsell system, has each color growing less saturated, from the outer edge of the wheel toward the center.

An accurate way of specifying color has been adopted by an organization called the Commission Internationale de l'Eclairage (CIE). This system is based on the very precise mixing of red, green, and blue. Any desired color can subsequently be made by mixing these colors in the defined proportions.

If scientists want to analyze the color of an existing object, they use an instrument called a photometer (foh-TAH-mee-tuhr). This measures light in the three wavelength ranges that correspond to the sensitivity of the three cone receptors in the eye. The color can be matched by mixing the three primary colors until the same photometer readings are reached.

CHECK THESE OUT!
✔ELECTROMAGNETIC SPECTRUM ✔LIGHT

Comet

A comet is a ball of rock, soil, and ice moving around the Solar System. When the comet's orbit (path) carries it close to the Sun, the heat can make the ice melt and boil off the comet's surface. This boiling leaves a trail of vapor and dust behind the comet, which reflects sunlight and appears as a spectacular tail.

The material that makes up comets was left over when the Sun, planets, and moons formed around 4.6 billion years ago. These larger objects swept up most of the rocky and icy debris (duh-BREE; broken pieces) that cluttered the Solar System at that time, but some was left over. Between the orbits of Mars and Jupiter, the leftover material formed the rocky asteroid belt. Farther out, a huge shell of icy material was left around the Solar System, far beyond the orbit of Pluto. These icy bodies collided to form comets. Astronomers believe these still lurk in space, in a region called the Oort (OHRT) Cloud.

Most comets can be found in this cloud, moving in roughly circular orbits around the Sun. They are so far away that they remain inactive. Astronomers cannot see the Oort Cloud because the comets are made mostly of ice with a little dark soot mixed in. Sometimes, though, the Solar System passes close to other stars as they move through space. The pull of gravity from these stars can disturb comets in the Oort Cloud, sending them falling toward the Sun.

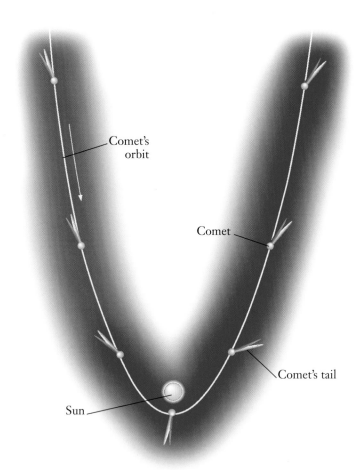

A comet moving in an elliptical orbit around the Sun. Its tail always points away from the Sun.

A comet's orbit is either a hyperbola (hy-PUHR-buh-luh), a path that will send it skimming past the Sun and then back out of the Solar System completely, or an ellipse (ih-LIPS), a stretched circle that brings the comet close to the Sun at one end and takes it far out into space at the other. Comets with ellipse-shaped orbits will eventually come back past the Sun, perhaps after a few years or a few million years.

Inside a comet

The solid center of a comet is called its nucleus, which can be anything from less than one mile (1.6 km) to a few dozen miles across. As its orbit brings the comet close to the Sun, the nucleus begins to heat up and the ice starts to evaporate into space. A cloud of vapor called the coma

---

HIGHLIGHTS

◆ Comets spend most of their time in the depths of outer space. They are visible to humans only if they come near Earth and the Sun.

◆ A comet is made of a solid nucleus, a huge halo of ice particles, and a tail that can stretch for millions of miles.

◆ Some comets are trapped in short-period orbits that bring them back past the Sun every few years.

forms around the nucleus. This coma can grow to 50,000 miles (80,000 km) across. Dust particles in the coma are carried away from the comet by the powerful solar wind. This material forms the comet's dust tail, which always points away from the Sun. When the comet has passed the Sun and moves away, it travels tail-first.

Each time the comet goes around the Sun, it loses some of its ice and dust, forming a meteor stream of tiny particles trailing around its orbit. If Earth crosses through this meteor stream and some of these particles fall into Earth's atmosphere, the particles burn up, forming meteors or shooting stars. Each comet has its own meteor stream, and meteor showers can be predicted for certain times of each year. When a comet's ice has all gone, the comet loses its striking appearance.

Famous comets

The most famous comet of all is Halley's Comet, which comes close to the Sun once every 76 years. It is named for British astronomer

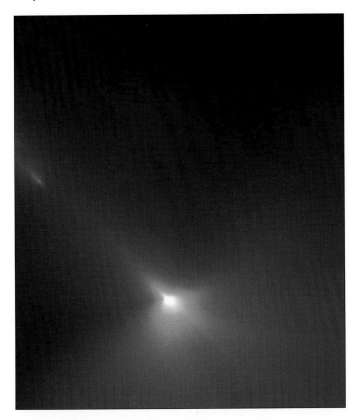

A false-color image of the comet Hale–Bopp showing its extremely hot center in white.

STORY OF SCIENCE

Discovering Comets

Comets often arrive without warning. Professional astronomers cannot spend all their time looking for them. Amateur astronomers can therefore make a real contribution by scanning the sky, often in the east before sunrise and in the west after sunset. If they identify a faint smudge of light, it could be the coma of a distant comet. The discoverer can report the find to the International Astronomical Union. Professional astronomers then turn their powerful telescopes on the comet—and the amateur gets the glory of having the comet named after him or her.

Sir Edmond Halley (1656–1742). In 1705, Halley realized that the comets seen in 1531, 1607, and 1682 were the same comet. He predicted the comet would return in 1758. He was right. It took six months for the dates of its return to be calculated by French mathematician Alexis Clairaut and French "astronomical computer" (a mathematician specializing in astronomy) Nicole-Reine Lepaute (1723–1788).

The earliest recorded sighting of Halley's Comet was in 240 B.C.E., and the comet is also shown on a tapestry from 1066. People have taken its appearance as a warning of coming disasters. Perhaps there is a good reason for this. Many scientists think a comet impact 65 million years ago helped wipe out the dinosaurs. Earth's surface is scattered with craters left after other comet impacts. The most recent impact was in 1908, when something (probably a small comet) exploded over Tunguska, Siberia, and flattened 772 square miles (2,000 sq km) of forest. In 1994, Comet Shoemaker–Levy 9 split apart and smashed into Jupiter with the most powerful explosions ever seen. Because the atmosphere of Jupiter is made of very dense gas, the comet fragments disappeared deep inside it without leaving any visible sign of impact. It would be a different story if a comet hit Earth.

CHECK THESE OUT!
✔ASTEROID ✔ASTRONOMY
✔METEOR ✔SOLAR SYSTEM ✔SUN

Compound

Substances that contain fixed proportions of two or more chemical elements

Atoms are the building blocks of all substances. If a substance contains only one kind of atom, it is called an element. Iron is one of the few elements that are familiar in everyday life. Most everyday substances are compounds because compounds are much more stable (unreactive) than atoms. Compounds are combinations of elements that are bound together in fixed proportions.

Both elements and compounds have very distinctive properties. They melt and boil at precise temperatures and they react with other elements and compounds in a predictable way. The chemical and physical properties of a compound are often completely different from the properties of the elements that make it up.

The atoms in a compound are linked together by bonds that are either ionic (eye-AH-nik) or covalent (KOH-VAY-luhnt). Some compounds have a mixture of these bonds.

HIGHLIGHTS

◆ When elements are bound together in fixed proportions they form compounds.

◆ The physical and chemical properties of a compound are different from the properties of the elements that make it up.

◆ Compounds can be loosely classified as ionic or covalent, depending on how their atoms are linked together.

Ionic compounds

Table salt is an ionic compound with equal amounts of sodium (chemical symbol Na) and chlorine (Cl). Its chemical name is sodium chloride. Pure sodium is a soft metal that can be cut using a knife. It melts at 208°F (98°C). Sodium reacts vigorously with many substances and explodes on contact with water. Chlorine is a toxic, greenish-yellow gas that reacts explosively with hydrogen in the presence of light. The melting point of chlorine is –150°F (–101°C).

When sodium and chlorine combine to produce salt, their individual properties vanish. Salt melts at a temperature of 1479°F (804°C), which is 1271°F (706°C) higher than the melting point of sodium and 1629°F (905°C) higher than that of chlorine. In addition, the chemical reactions of sodium chloride are nowhere near as vigorous as those of either sodium or chlorine.

Atoms have a positively charged nucleus (NOO-klee-uhs; center) with negatively charged electrons around it that balance out the positive nucleus. If an atom loses one electron, it becomes a positive ion. That is what happens to the sodium atoms in sodium chloride. The chlorine gains the electron to become a negatively charged chloride ion. The symbol for the sodium ion is Na^+ and the symbol for the chloride

A sodium chloride lattice. Chlorine is shown in green and sodium is red.

ion is Cl⁻. With equal numbers of each type of ion, the positive and negative charges balance.

In solid sodium chloride, these ions alternate with each other, so that each sodium ion is surrounded by chlorine ions, and each chlorine ion is surrounded by sodium ions. This structure is called a lattice. Since the two types of ions have opposite charges, they attract each other strongly with bonds called ionic bonds.

The high melting point of sodium chloride is caused by the strong attraction between ions of opposite charges in the solid lattice. Large amounts of heat energy are needed to break down the lattice, which is what happens when an ionic solid melts. This happens only at high temperatures.

Molecular compounds

Glucose is the simple sugar made by most plants. It consists of definite groups of atoms called molecules (MAH-lih-KYOOLZ). Each molecule contains 6 carbon atoms (symbol C), 12 hydrogen atoms (symbol H), and 6 oxygen atoms (symbol O), so the formula of glucose is written $C_6H_{12}O_6$.

The atoms in each molecule are held together tightly by bonds called covalent bonds. In a

As living organisms grow, they make new compounds, and as they decay, these compounds are broken down to be made into others.

covalent bond, electrons do not move over to another atom as they do in an ionic bond. Instead, the electrons pair up between two atoms. So a single covalent bond is one pair of electrons that is shared between the atoms that it holds together.

Molecular compounds, like ionic compounds, have properties that are different from their component elements. The elements in glucose are carbon, which is the main component of coal, and hydrogen and oxygen, which are both gases.

Polyatomic ions

Not all compounds can be classified as simply ionic or molecular. Some compounds contain polyatomic ions, ions made up of groups of atoms that are held together by covalent bonds. A simple example of such a compound is sodium sulfate (Na_2SO_4). The sodium ions (Na^+) in this salt are identical to those in sodium chloride. However, in each sulfate ion (SO_4^{2-}) four oxygen atoms are linked to one sulfur atom by covalent bonds, and the result is a negative ion. The sulfate ion has a double negative charge because it has two more electrons than the individual atoms would have.

Polyatomic ions can contain large numbers of atoms. For example, ethylenediamine tetra-acetate (EDTA) has the chemical formula $C_2H_4N_2(CH_3COO)_4^-$. Because of its size it is used to remove lead and radioactive metals from the bloodstreams of victims of poisoning.

CHECK THESE OUT!
✔ATOM ✔CHEMICAL REACTION ✔ELEMENT
✔MOLECULE ✔PHYSICAL CHANGE
✔SALTS

Constellation

Group of stars representing objects from everyday life and mythology

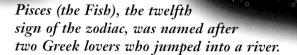

Since ancient times, people have looked up at the stars in the night sky and made patterns out of them, such as figures of familiar objects, animals, or people. These patterns, called constellations, are used to divide the sky for easy reference. Constellations are therefore important in astronomy (the study of the planets and the stars).

Origin of the constellations

From Egypt to Greece and from Mexico to China, different civilizations selected their own constellation patterns for thousands of years. Ideas and star patterns often moved from one culture to another. The Egyptians, for example, recognized Ursa Major, the Great Bear, although there were no bears in Egypt. However, around the year 150 C.E., Greek astronomer Ptolemy listed 48 star patterns in his book the *Almagest*. This list was adopted throughout the western

Pisces (the Fish), the twelfth sign of the zodiac, was named after two Greek lovers who jumped into a river.

world and it still forms the basis of today's constellations. During the 17th and 18th centuries, astronomers had the first chance to travel south of the equator and see stars only visible from the southern hemisphere. Many astronomers invented new constellations and there was a great deal of confusion between different maps. Astronomers finally agreed to 40 new constellations, bringing the number to 88.

What is a constellation?

A constellation is a pattern made of individual stars. For example, the Little Bear, Ursa Minor, is made of seven stars. The stars do not need to have any real association with each other; they just happen to lie in the same part of the sky as seen from Earth. Often the stars in a constellation will be hundreds or even thousands of light-years from each other. If viewers could shift their point of view to somewhere else in the galaxy, the pattern would no longer exist.

Also, because the stars are moving through space in different directions, the constellation patterns are only temporary. In thousands of years time, few of the familiar patterns recognized today will survive.

Today's constellations have to be defined in a different way. Astronomers need to know to which constellation stars and other celestial objects belong, even if they cannot be fitted into

HIGHLIGHTS

◆ Different ancient people saw different constellations in the sky, but the patterns used today have developed from the star maps of the ancient Greeks.

◆ Today, constellations are defined as areas of sky rather than just particular stars, so every object in the sky belongs to a constellation.

◆ Because of Earth's rotation, the sky seems to spin around two fixed points, the north and south celestial poles.

◆ Constellations close enough to a pole will not set and are circumpolar.

Star Stories

Many of the constellations are named after characters from Greek and Roman legends, but there are two large groups of constellations that are associated with a single story. One of these stories is centered around the large constellation of Pegasus, the Flying Horse. Pegasus belonged to a Greek hero called Perseus, who rescued Andromeda, the daughter of Queen Cassiopeia and King Cepheus, from a ferocious sea monster, Cetus. All of these characters are preserved as constellations in the summer sky of the northern hemisphere.

Another group of constellations appears in the northern winter sky. Orion, the hunter, is fighting Taurus, the Bull. Behind Orion stand his hunting dogs Canis Major (the Great Dog, which contains Sirius, the brightest star in the sky) and Canis Minor (the Little Dog). At his feet Lepus, the Hare, is hiding. In the Greek legend Orion was killed by a scorpion, preserved as the constellation Scorpio on the opposite side of the sky to Orion.

one of the easily recognized patterns, and even if they are only visible through telescopes. In 1930, astronomers of the International Astronomical Union invented a new way of defining constellations using imaginary boundary lines across the sky. Stars within each boundary are given names that indicate their brightness in the constellation. The 24 brightest stars are named from the Greek alphabet (alpha, beta, and so on), and fainter stars are given numbers. The brightest stars have also kept their traditional Arabic names. The result of this system is that the limits of the constellations are now fixed. Every star in the sky belongs to one of the 88 constellations.

The moving sky

The constellation patterns remain the same for thousands of years, but the sky overhead constantly changes because of the way Earth spins on its axis every day and orbits the Sun once a year. If Earth's rotation could be stopped, it could be seen that the changing point of view makes the Sun trace a path against the background constellations once a year. The line through the sky that the Sun moves along is called the ecliptic (ih-KLIP-tik). The ecliptic is the plane that runs through the Sun and Earth's orbit, and out through the Solar System.

As Earth rotates every day, the Sun seems to rise on the eastern horizon, pass across the

southern part of the sky (as seen from the northern hemisphere), and set in the west. Because the Sun is so bright, it hides the constellations near it in the sky, so the stars are visible only after sunset. The sky seems to pivot around the points directly above the North

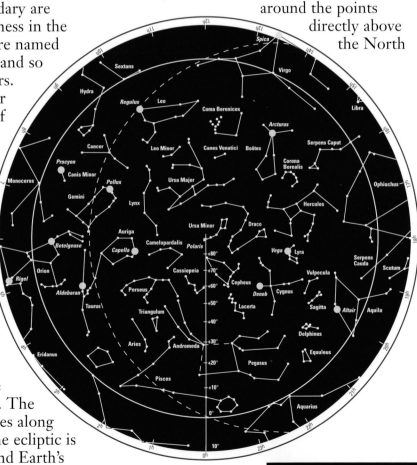

The constellations of the north polar hemisphere.

● Stars of the first magnitude
- - - Ecliptic
— Celestial equator

and South Poles, called the celestial (suh-LES-chuhl) poles. From each hemisphere, only one celestial pole can be seen. As one gets closer to the equator, the pole sinks lower on the horizon. Constellations close enough to the pole never set (are always visible) and are circumpolar (move in circles around the pole).

Familiar constellations

The most important circumpolar constellations in the northern sky are Cassiopeia, Ursa Minor (the Little Bear), and Ursa Major (the Great Bear). The brightest stars in both the bears have roughly the same pattern—four stars at the end making up a rough rectangle, with three stars in a chain from one corner. The bear's body is represented by the square of stars, the tail is made by the chain. Fainter stars represent the head and legs. Today, the shape looks more like a spoon or saucepan, and so the constellations are often called the Big and Little Dippers.

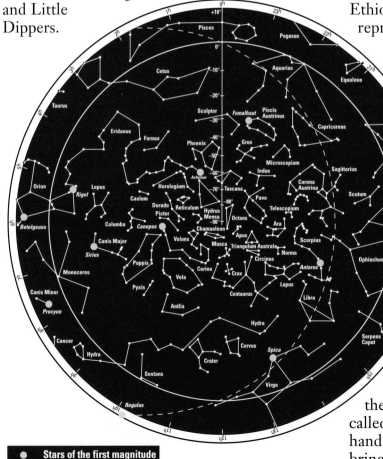

The constellations of the south polar hemisphere.

Legend:
- ● Stars of the first magnitude
- - - - Ecliptic
- ── Celestial equator

The Big Dipper is probably the most familiar of all the constellations. It hangs high overhead on winter evenings in the northern hemisphere. The two stars farthest from the dipper's handle are called the Pointers. A direct line through them points to a star on the end of the Little Dipper's handle. This star is not especially bright, but it is very important. It is Polaris, the Pole Star. By coincidence it lies very close to the position of the north celestial pole, where the sky seems to pivot.

Because Polaris always stays close to the same place in the sky, people have used it for thousands of years to navigate. Polaris always lies due north in the sky. Because it is directly overhead at the North Pole, the further south one travels, the closer to the horizon Polaris gets, until the star vanishes south of the equator.

Cassiopeia lies on the opposite side of Polaris to the Big Dipper. It is a bright W shape of stars, named after a mythical (imaginary) Queen of Ethiopia, whose husband and daughter are also represented in the stars.

Farther away from the pole star, the constellations rise and set every day. Because of the way the Sun moves through them as seen from Earth, different times of year are best for seeing particular groups of stars. In the northern hemisphere these are the times when a constellation is at its highest in the southern sky just after it gets dark.

Following the pointer stars of the Big Dipper away from the Pole Star will bring the constellation of Leo into view. This constellation is one of the few that really does look like the thing it is supposed to, in this case a sitting lion. Leo is best seen during spring.

In summer, when Cassiopeia is high overhead and the Big Dipper is low down in the north, the sky is dominated by a pattern called the summer triangle. Following the right hand stroke of the W in Cassiopeia upward will bring into view Deneb, the brightest star in Cygnus (SIG-nuhs; a cross-shaped constellation representing a swan). The top-right-hand star in

The 12 Constellations of the Zodiac

As Earth moves around the Sun each year, the Sun seems to follow a circular path around the sky called the ecliptic. The other planets also orbit in roughly the same plane as Earth, so they also seem to move through the ecliptic. The region of sky in which the Sun and planets can appear is called the zodiac, from a Greek phrase meaning "circle of animals," because all but one of the 12 main constellations it contains represent animals. These constellations are Aries (the Ram), Taurus (the Bull), Gemini (the Twins), Cancer (the Crab), Leo (the Lion), Virgo (the Virgin), Libra (the Balance), Scorpio (the Scorpion), Sagittarius (the Archer), Capricorn (the Sea Goat), Aquarius (the Water Carrier), and Pisces (the Fish).

In reality, the zodiac is a little more complicated than this. At certain times, the planets can pass through other constellations, and a thirteenth constellation, Ophiuchus, also crosses the ecliptic, so that the Sun passes through it each year. Astrologers who use the zodiac to supposedly foretell the future usually ignore these complications. Most astrologers use calculated positions of the Sun against the zodiac based on Ptolemy's book. These positions are now incorrect by about one month because of a slow wobble in Earth's axis of rotation. This wobble causes the length of the year, as measured from one spring equinox (EE-kwuh-nahks; around March 21) to the next, to be slightly different than the time for one full revolution of Earth around the Sun.

the triangle is Deneb. The others are Vega, at top left, in the constellation Lyra, named for an ancient musical instrument, and Altair, a reddish star closer to the horizon, in Aquila, the Eagle.

The largest constellation in the autumn sky is Pegasus, the Flying Horse. The constellation looks nothing like a horse but is easily spotted because its brightest stars form a large square. From the upper-left corner of the square, a trail of stars forms Andromeda, the Princess. This constellation contains the Andromeda Galaxy, which is larger than the Milky Way and so distant it takes light 2.2 million light-years to reach it. The Andromeda Galaxy is the most distant object that can be seen without the use of binoculars.

The winter sky is the most spectacular of all, dominated by Orion, the brightest constellation in the sky, and its surrounding group. Orion represents a hunter from Greek myth. Three bright stars mark his belt, the bright red Betelgeuse is his shoulder, and the brilliant white Rigel is his knee. A row of stars hanging from the belt make Orion's sword. They include a fuzzy patch of light called the Orion Nebula, which is a huge cloud of gas and dust where stars are being born. The Orion Nebula is one of the few nebulas that can be seen with the unaided eye. Orion faces Taurus, the Bull.

A triangle of stars marks the bull's face and horns. The Pleiades, a cluster of young stars only about 60 million years old, mark its shoulders.

Some constellations can only be seen from south of the equator and are circumpolar around the southern celestial pole. The best known of these constellations is Crux, the Southern Cross. It is a small constellation on the Milky Way, close to the south celestial pole, with four bright stars forming an irregular cross.

CHECK THESE OUT!

✔ASTRONOMY ✔COSMOLOGY ✔GALAXY
✔MILKY WAY ✔STAR ✔UNIVERSE

Taurus, the bull, is the second sign of the zodiac.

Continent

The major landmasses of Earth, largely or entirely surrounded by oceans

The dry ground of Earth is divided into six continental landmasses: North America, South America, Eurasia (Europe and Asia), Africa, Australasia, and Antarctica. Geographically, this classification also covers the islands off their coasts. Australasia, for example, includes both the main continental mass of Australia and the islands of New Zealand. Antarctica is the only continent that is completely covered by ice. Only Australia, New Zealand, and Antarctica are surrounded entirely by ocean. North and South America are joined by the isthmus (IS-muhs) of Panama. Eurasia and Africa are joined by the Arabian peninsula. Just over two-thirds of the total continental land area is currently in the Northern Hemisphere.

There is more land to a continent than that showing above the ocean surface. A fringe zone, called the continental margin, is under water. This margin slopes down from sea level to the deep ocean floor. Continents and the ocean floor are made of different materials.

HIGHLIGHTS

- There are six continental landmasses on Earth today: North America, South America, Eurasia, Africa, Australasia, and Antarctica.

- Scientists believe they formed, many millions of years ago, from the breakup of a single supercontinent, named Pangaea.

- Moving tectonic plates on Earth's crust carried the continents to their present position.

- These plates can move apart or collide, continuing to change the shape of continents.

Continental formation

Geologists believe Earth began forming about 4.6 billion years ago. The continents and oceans probably developed some tens of millions of years after this. Scientists believe Earth's crust was molten at this time, allowing lighter material to float through it to the surface. The continents are made mostly of granite and related rock, which are lighter, while the ocean floor is made of heavier rocks, such as basalt and gabbro.

Scientists have wondered for centuries whether all of Earth's landmasses might once have been joined as one. As early as 1620, English philosopher Francis Bacon (1561–1626) pointed out that, on a map, the coastlines of South America and Africa seemed to fit together. In the early 1900s, German geophysicist Alfred Wegener (1880–1930) suggested that the landmasses started as a single supercontinent in a vast ocean in the Southern Hemisphere, which he named Pangaea (PAN-jee-uh). Many millions of years ago, Pangaea broke apart to form the separate continents. Wegener said that similar rocks and fossils found in the different present-day continents supported his theory. For example, the oldest rocks of northwest Scotland are very similar to the rocks of eastern Canada.

Wegener argued that a process he called continental drift produced the breakaway and movement of the continents, but he could not

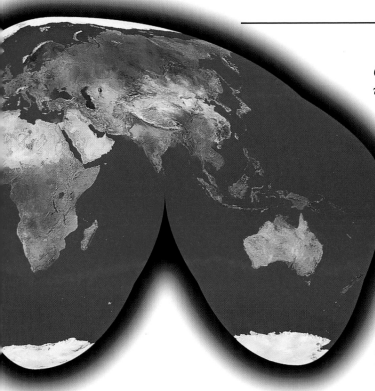

Continents are the landmasses that are visible above the oceans that surround them.

200 million years ago. It formed two large pieces, which have been named Laurasia and Gondwana, separated by an ocean named the Tethys. Laurasia later moved north and westward and broke into North America, Europe, and much of Asia. Gondwana separated into South America, Africa, India, Antarctica, and Australasia. As North America moved away from Europe, and South America from Africa, the Atlantic Ocean was formed. Meanwhile, Africa and Europe moved closer together, and what was left of the Tethys became the Mediterranean Sea. Finally, India was forced together with Asia.

As the plates move

As two tectonic plates move apart, liquid rock from inside Earth rises to the surface. When the rock has cooled, it forms a new continental margin. This is called a constructive process.

When two different plates collide, one usually begins to slide below the other. This forces material to pile upward. A different type of continental margin is produced, called a destructive margin. For example, if a light continental plate and a heavier oceanic plate collide, the oceanic plate will move below the continental plate. This is an example of a destructive margin.

The Himalayan mountains, north of India, are the result of a collision zone where two continental plates (India and Eurasia) have come together, destroying the ocean that was once between them. These two plates are still moving.

In the future, the continents will continue to change. Erosion will wear down high mountains, gradually making them lower. At the same time, plate movements are likely to continue to rearrange whole continents or at least parts of them. In addition, global warming may cause polar ice to melt, raising the level of the oceans and flooding many low-lying coastal areas.

explain how it happened. Since the 1960s, however, geophysicists (scientists who study Earth's physical processes) have discovered that Earth's crust is made of some 12 rigid tectonic plates. These plates float across the planet's surface and carry whole continents with them. Most plates move about 1 inch (2.5 cm) per year, and rates greater than 7 inches (17.5 cm) per year have been recorded. Today, most scientists believe Pangaea first broke apart about

LOOK CLOSER

Fossil Evidence

Fossilized (preserved) creatures very similar to one another are found on continents separated by oceans, such as Africa and South America. Dating these fossils has helped geophysicists figure out when the different pieces of Pangaea broke away. For example, fossils of a primitive reptile called *Lystrosaurus* have been found in North America, India, Africa, and Antarctica. This reptile could not have crossed the oceans, so at one time all these landmasses must have been joined. Most scientists also believe that the evolution of many different mammal species was encouraged by the moving apart of the continents. Certain groups of animals became isolated and evolved in different ways.

CHECK THESE OUT!
✔CONTINENTAL SHELF ✔FAULT ✔GONDWANA
✔PANGAEA ✔PLATE TECTONICS ✔ROCK

Continental Shelf

Margin of continents that lies below sea level between the shoreline and shelf slope

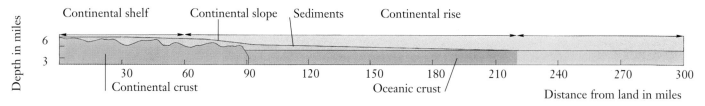

The continental shelf descends gradually away from dry land to form the continental slope, which is quite steep, and the continental rise.

The edges of continents that are covered by shallow shelf seas no more than 600 feet (200 m) deep are called continental shelves. The width of the shelves varies from less than a mile (1.6 km) to hundreds of miles, although the average is about 40 miles (65 km) wide. The marine life of the shelf seabed and the waters above them provide some of the world's most economically important fisheries, such as the Grand Banks off Newfoundland. The buried sands, muds, and limestones of the shelves also contain some of the world's most important reserves of oil and gas.

The edge of the continental shelf is marked by a break in the slope of the seabed. Beyond its outer edge, the shelf slopes at an average of five degrees to the ocean floor over 12,000 feet (4,000 m) below. In places, for example off the west coast of the Americas, the shelf is extremely narrow and slopes steeply down into an ocean trench. Here the ocean floor has been dragged down below the edge of the continent during destructive plate tectonic movement of Earth's crust, called subduction (SUHB-DUHK-shuhn).

Formation of continental shelves

Mud and sand are continuously deposited by rivers onto continental shelves. Over millions of years, sediments (SEH-duh-muhnts) have piled up into layers thousands of feet thick. The layers form fringing wedges that extend many miles out into the oceans. The width of a continental shelf depends on the sea level and tectonic processes.

At present so much water is locked up in the polar ice caps that global sea levels are relatively low. Consequently the continental shelves are

generally narrow. During the last ice age, about 10,000 years ago, the sea level fell by up to 330 feet (100 m), turning many of the continental shelves into dry land. In earlier times the sea levels were relatively high. Much larger areas of the continental margins were submerged and so much wider continental shelves formed. In warm waters, wide shelves allow the extensive growth of coral reefs and the formation of limey sediments full of the shelly remains of sea creatures. Where shelf seas are very shallow and climates are very hot, seawater is evaporated. Layered deposits of minerals such as salt or gypsum (JIP-suhm) may form, as happened millions of years ago in the Mediterranean Sea.

Where the continental shelf sea life has been abundant, the organic remains of the organisms may be buried in such large numbers in the seabed sediments that they eventually form fossil (FAH-suhl) fuels such as oil and gas. Huge oil and gas reserves, for example, have been extracted from the continental shelf around the British Isles in recent years.

The edge of the continental shelves may be cut by numerous submarine canyons. These submerged valleys have been eroded by a type of gravity-controlled flow called a turbidity current. The currents carry mud and silt from the shelf down the slope and out to the deep sea floor.

CHECK THESE OUT!
✔CONTINENT ✔OIL ✔PLATE TECTONICS

Glossary

axis (AK-suhs) Imaginary line through a planet around which the planet revolves.

continental plate Section of Earth's crust that carries a landmass. *See also* oceanic plate.

deposit (dih-PAH-zuht) Matter laid down by a natural process.

Earth's crust Outer layer of Earth, mostly made up of crystalline rocks.

ecliptic (ih-KLIP-tik) Plane around the Sun in which Earth orbits.

evolution (EH-vuh-LOO-shuhn) How living organisms adapt over millions of years to changes in their environment.

fault (FAWLT) Fracture in Earth's crust causing the displacement of crust on one or both sides of the fracture.

fermentation (FUHR-muhn-TAY-shuhn) Chemical change producing fizz.

fertilizer (FUHR-tuhl-EYE-zuhr) Substance added to soil to improve its ability to support plant growth.

fiber (FY-buhr) Thread or a thread-shaped object.

filter Sheet of material or a substance such as sand through which gas or liquid is passed to separate out suspended material.

fissure (FIH-shuhr) Long crack.

fossil fuel (FAH-suhl FYOO-uhl) Fuel formed from fossilized organisms, such as coal or oil.

friction (FRIK-shuhn) Force that resists relative motion between two objects in contact.

hemisphere (HEH-muh-SFIR) Half of a ball-shaped object.

horizon (huh-RY-zuhn) Apparent boundary between the sky and the land or sea.

hyperbola (hy-PUHR-buh-luh) U-shaped curve.

ice cap All-year-round covering of ice and snow.

impervious (im-PUHR-vee-uhs) incapable of being penetrated. Water cannot seep into impervious rock.

impurities (im-PYOOR-uh-teez) Unwanted substances present in a mineral, which are removed to obtain a pure element.

inertia (ih-NUHR-shuh) the tendency of matter to keep moving in the same way until affected by an outside force.

oceanic plate Section of Earth's crust that carries a large body of water. *See also* continental plate.

orbit Path of an object around a larger object, determined by the gravity of the larger object.

organic Containing carbon and hydrogen; derived from living or once-living matter.

polarize (POH-luh-RYZ) To break up into groups that repel one another.

precipitation (prih-SIH-puh-TAY-shuhn) Water falling from clouds as rain, sleet, snow, or hail.

predator Animal that kills and eats other animals.

radioactive decay Disintegration of the nucleus of a radioactive atom or isotope.

ratio (RAY-shoh) Relationship in size or amount between two or more things.

silt Fine-grained deposit in the water. *See also* deposit.

spectrum Ordered arrangement of the different wavelengths of sound or light.

tremor (TREH-muhr) Quiver or tremble in Earth's surface just before or after an earthquake.

velocity (vuh-LAH-suh-tee) How quickly an object moves in a certain direction.

voltage (VOHL-tij) Electrical potential energy that can be converted into another form. Expressed in volts.

warm-blooded Having a high and constant body temperature.

Index

Page numbers in **boldface type** refer to main
articles and their illustrations. Page numbers
in *italic type* refer to additional illustrations.

550	Exploring Earth and
EXP	Space Science
#2	

05/06	**DATE DUE**